Reading Skills
7-8

Written by
Denise Skomer

Editor: Collene Dobelmann
Illustrator: Corbin Hillam
Designer: Moonhee Pak
Cover Designer: Barbara Peterson
Art Director: Tom Cochrane
Project Director: Carolea Williams

Table of Contents

Introduction 4

Synonyms and Antonyms
Naming Pairs 5
Word Match 6
Story Time Synonyms 7
Interesting Words 8

Prefixes, Suffixes, and Root Words
Prefix Skills 9
Suffix Skills. 10
Breaking Words. 11
Crossword Puzzler. 12

Confusing Words
Definition Decision 13
Sentence Sense 14
Make the Right Choice. 15
Correct or Incorrect?. 16

Analogies
Finding Analogies. 17
Figure It Out 18
Analogy Puzzler 19
Mind Challenge. 20

Figurative Language
Everyday Idioms 21
Select a Simile 22
Movie Metaphors 23
Identifying Figurative Language 24

Homophones and Homographs
Homophones. 25
Letter Home 26
Homographs 27
Homograph Logic. 28

Context Clues
Conquering Context Clues 29
Meaning Sleuth. 30

Reading for Clues 31
Dictionary Detective 32

Classifying Events and Ideas
Human Body Classification. 33
Classify Details. 34
Classified Ads. 35
Classifying History. 36

Sequencing
Story Ordering. 37
Note Card Mix-Up 38
What's the Order?. 39
Order the Steps. 40

Following Directions
Brownie Recipe 41
Using a Flowchart 42
Map It!. 43
Code Breaker. 44

Cause and Effect
Find the Cause or Effect. 45
Just Because. 46
Frederick Douglass 47
The American Revolution. 48

Making Inferences
Inference Practice 49
What a Character! 50
What's Happening?. 51
Infer the Meaning. 52

Fact and Opinion
Which Is Which? 53
Identifying Fact and Opinion. 54
Sorting Facts and Opinions 55
Analyze an Editorial 56

Summarizing
Story Summary 57

Movie Buff. 58
Sum It Up. 59
Short Summaries. 60

Point of View
First or Third 61
First to Third; Third to First 62
Fairy Tale Views. 63
Pick a Point 64

Drawing Conclusions
What Do They Want?. 65
What's Happening?. 66
What's the Word?. 67
Experimental Conclusions. 68

Main Idea and Supporting Details
It's All in the Title 69
Name the Article. 70
Main Idea. 71
Statement Identification 72
Which One Doesn't Belong? 73
Volunteer Persuasion 74

Predicting Outcomes
What Happened Next?. 75
And Then. 76
What Is That About?. 77
More Predictions. 78

Story Elements
Who and Where? 79
Dialogue Drawings. 80
It's All About the Moral 81
Plot Line. 82

Using Text Organizers
Reading a Table of Contents 83
Using a Glossary 84
Using an Index 85
Understanding a Bibliography. 86

Interpreting Graphic Organizers
Interpreting a Bar Graph 87
Interpreting Charts. 88
Interpreting a Table 89
Interpreting a Timeline. 90
Interpreting a Diagram 91

Using Reference Materials
Using a Thesaurus. 92
Using a Dictionary. 93
Using an Internet Search Engine 94
Using an Encyclopedia 95
Using References. 96

Consumer Reading
Reading a Coupon 97
Reading a Recipe 98
Reading a Train Route 99
Reading an Advertisement. 100
Reading a Promotional Offer. 101

Analyze Narrative Texts
Analyzing Poetry. 102
Analyzing a Journal Entry 103
Analyzing a Personal Narrative 104
Analyzing a Biography 105

Analyze Expository Texts
Analyzing a Business Letter 106
Analyzing a How-to Passage 107
Analyzing a Newspaper Article 108
Analyzing a Compare/Contrast Passage. . . 109

Content Area Reading
Math 110
Social Studies. 111
Science. 112
Health 113
Art 114

Answer Key 115

Introduction

Each book in the *Power Practice*™ series contains dozens of ready-to-use activity pages to provide students with skill practice. The fun activities can be used to supplement and enhance what you are already teaching in your classroom. Give an activity page to students as independent class work, or send the pages home as homework to reinforce skills taught in class. An answer key is included at the end of each book to provide verification of student responses.

The practical and creative activities in the reading skills books provide the perfect practice with over 20 reading skills. Each book is divided into sections covering these various skills.

Reading Skills 7–8 provides activities that will directly assist students in practicing and reinforcing skills such as
• prefixes, suffixes, and root words
• analogies
• figurative language
• context clues
• point of view
• using reference materials
• cause and effect
• story elements
• main idea and details

The final four sections of the book give students practice with reading narrative texts, expository texts, consumer reading materials, and content area materials. The questions in these sections are designed to cover the various skills students practiced throughout the book. These applications give them a chance to apply the skills and provide a means for assessing their progress.

Use these ready-to-go activities to "recharge" skill review and give students the power to succeed!

Naming Pairs

SYNONYMS AND ANTONYMS

A **synonym** is a word that means the same or about the same as another word.
Examples: peaceful/calm   clear/transparent
An **antonym** is a word that means the opposite of another word.
Examples: arrive/depart   friendly/hostile

Circle **synonyms** or **antonyms** to identify each pair of words.

1	sweet/sour	synonyms	antonyms
2	frigid/scalding	synonyms	antonyms
3	optimistic/hopeful	synonyms	antonyms
4	plentiful/barren	synonyms	antonyms
5	hectic/frantic	synonyms	antonyms
6	bright/dull	synonyms	antonyms
7	ancient/aged	synonyms	antonyms
8	ally/enemy	synonyms	antonyms
9	meticulous/careless	synonyms	antonyms
10	numerous/many	synonyms	antonyms
11	chuckle/giggle	synonyms	antonyms
12	strange/unusual	synonyms	antonyms

Write a sentence that includes a pair of words from above.

_____

_____

Reading Skills • 7–8 © 2004 Creative Teaching Press

Word Match

SYNONYMS AND ANTONYMS

shut	damp	disrespectful	hinder
open	assist	timid	dry
soothe	flunk	bold	destroy
pass	provoke	polite	sufficient
deficient	keep	freeze	scald

Use the words in the word box to complete the chart.

		Synonyms	Antonyms
1	moist		
2	adequate		
3	fail		
4	rude		
5	shy		
6	burn		
7	help		
8	aggravate		
9	preserve		
10	close		

Reading Skills • 7–8 © 2004 Creative Teaching Press

Name _____ Date _____

Story Time Synonyms

Synonyms and Antonyms

Read each story or nursery rhyme title in Column A. Read each description in Column B. Write the letter of the description that matches each title. Look for synonym clues.

Column A

1 _____ *London Bridge Is Falling Down*

2 _____ *Little Red Riding Hood*

3 _____ *Row, Row, Row Your Boat*

4 _____ *Mary Had a Little Lamb*

5 _____ *It's Raining, It's Pouring*

6 _____ *Little Red Hen*

7 _____ *Peter, Peter Pumpkin Eater*

8 _____ *Rain, Rain, Go Away*

9 _____ *The Ugly Duckling*

10 _____ *Jack and the Beanstalk*

11 _____ *Twinkle, Twinkle Little Star*

12 _____ *Jack Be Nimble, Jack Be Quick*

13 _____ *Old MacDonald Had a Farm*

14 _____ *The Itsy Bitsy Spider*

Column B

a. The girl with the crimson cloak

b. A gourd-devouring boy

c. An unattractive bird

d. Teeny, tiny arachnid

e. Small, sparkling celestial body

f. A limber boy with great speed

g. A female chicken who is small and scarlet

h. A boy and his legume stem

i. A shower, a downpour

j. The destruction of a connecting link in England

k. A girl and her young sheep

l. An elderly man and his plantation

m. Drizzle, sprinkle, please leave

n. Paddle that vessel

15 Use synonyms to write a description that fits the title.

The Brave Little Tailor _____

Name _____ Date _____

Interesting Words

SYNONYMS AND ANTONYMS

Write two synonyms and two antonyms for each word. Be creative with your choices.

Synonyms   **Antonyms**

1 _____   difficult   **3** _____

2 _____   **4** _____

5 _____   cold   **7** _____

6 _____   **8** _____

9 _____   scared   **11** _____

10 _____   **12** _____

13 _____   dark   **15** _____

14 _____   **16** _____

17 _____   heavy   **19** _____

18 _____   **20** _____

21 _____   joyful   **23** _____

22 _____   **24** _____

Reading Skills • 7–8 © 2004 Creative Teaching Press

 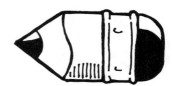

Prefix Skills

PREFIXES, SUFFIXES, AND ROOT WORDS

Prefix	Meaning
mono-	one
poly-	many
un-	not
re-	again
inter-	between
sub-	under
ex-	out
pre-	before
post-	after
mis-	wrongly, badly

Use the information in the chart to help you determine the meaning of each word. Write the letter of the definition that matches each word.

1. _____ uncertain

2. _____ monorail

3. _____ postoperative

4. _____ extract

5. _____ subway

6. _____ reinvent

7. _____ polygon

8. _____ international

9. _____ prejudge

10. _____ misinterpret

a. to remove or take out

b. to understand wrongly

c. to make a decision before

d. a many-sided figure

e. to create again

f. not sure

g. between nations

h. done after surgery

i. a train that travels underground

j. a single rail serving as a track

Name _____ Date _____

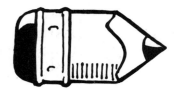 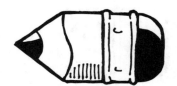

Suffix Skills
PREFIXES, SUFFIXES, AND ROOT WORDS

Suffix	Meaning
-ful	full of
-ment	action, result
-able, -ible	able, capable of
-less	lacking, without
-ian	one skilled in
-ness	quality, state, or condition of
-ist	one who works at or practices
-er, -or	person, doer
-ly	like
-ward	direction

Use the information in the chart to help you determine the meaning of each word. Write the letter of the definition that matches each word.

1 _____ backward

2 _____ chemist

3 _____ sorrowful

4 _____ affordable

5 _____ politician

6 _____ kingly

7 _____ blameless

8 _____ shipment

9 _____ gardener

10 _____ seriousness

a. innocent; without fault

b. goods that are sent

c. like royalty

d. state of being somber

e. person who grows things

f. one who works with chemicals

g. moving in reverse direction

h. full of sadness

i. able to be bought

j. one skilled in government

Reading Skills • 7–8 © 2004 Creative Teaching Press

Name _____ Date _____

Breaking Words
Prefixes, Suffixes, and Root Words

Rewrite each word by breaking apart the root word and the prefix or suffix. The first one is done for you.

1 fanciful = _____ fancy _____ + _____ ful _____

2 breakable = _____ + _____

3 smokiness = _____ + _____

4 mistreat = _____ + _____

5 happily = _____ + _____

6 musician = _____ + _____

7 homeward = _____ + _____

8 nonsense = _____ + _____

9 bicycle = _____ + _____

10 geologist = _____ + _____

11 historian = _____ + _____

12 juror = _____ + _____

13 react = _____ + _____

14 indoor = _____ + _____

15 changeable = _____ + _____

16 theorist = _____ + _____

17 interact = _____ + _____

18 paraphrase = _____ + _____

19 friendship = _____ + _____

20 submarine = _____ + _____

Name _____ Date _____

Crossword Puzzler

PREFIXES, SUFFIXES, AND ROOT WORDS

pseudonym	simplify	nontoxic
triangle	salvage	natural
geology	actress	retrospective

Use what you know about prefixes, suffixes, and root words to match each word in the word box to the correct clue. Use the words to complete the crossword puzzle.

Across
3. Not poisonous
7. A female performer
8. Looking backwards
9. The study of the earth

Down
1. Act of saving
2. Relating to the environment
4. A three-sided figure
5. A false name
6. Make easy

Reading Skills • 7–8 © 2004 Creative Teaching Press

Definition Decision

CONFUSING WORDS

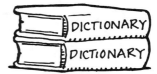

Some words are often confused with other words. Misusing these confusing words will change the meaning of a sentence and can often lead to embarrassing errors. Read the example below:

The camel lives in the **dessert**.   The camel lives in the **desert**.

The first sentence makes you think about a camel in your ice cream. The second sentence correctly uses the word "desert," meaning a dry, barren region.

Read each pair of commonly confused words. Draw a line from each word to its definition.

1 personnel	private
2 personal	employees, staff
3 bibliography	a list of authors' works
4 biography	a written history of a person's life
5 decent	process of moving down
6 descent	good; having strong morals
7 recent	to feel annoyed
8 resent	current
9 devise	to plan
10 device	a piece of equipment
11 access	more than needed
12 excess	ability to enter

Name _____ Date _____

Sentence Sense

CONFUSING WORDS

Circle the word that correctly completes each sentence.

1 Remember to use a (capital, capitol) letter to begin each sentence.

2 Maria (passed, past) her geography test.

3 My parents gave me (advice, advise) about which sport to play.

4 Jacob is taller (than, then) Michael.

5 Listen to your (conscience, conscious) and make a good decision.

6 Be careful not to (loose, lose) your keys.

7 Which movie did you (choose, chose) to see?

8 Everyone was asked to stay seated (accept, except) Kevin.

9 Exercising has a positive (effect, affect) on your health.

10 The girl decided to (lay, lie) on the couch.

11 Please (raise, rise) to sing the school song.

12 Being successful requires (cooperation, corporation) and teamwork.

13 I asked my brother to (lend, loan) me money for lunch.

14 I live (further, farther) from the school than my best friend.

15 I can (assure, ensure) you that we have done our best.

16 Please give me your most (recent, resent) school picture.

17 The athlete was (confidant, confident) in her ability to perform.

18 Mark created a (devise, device) that would turn the light on and off.

19 The surprise birthday party turned out (good, well).

20 Adam did a (through, thorough) job of cleaning his desk.

Reading Skills • 7–8 © 2004 Creative Teaching Press

Name _____ Date _____

Make the Right Choice

CONFUSING WORDS

raise	rise	lay	lie	wonder
desert	dessert	affect	effect	wander

Complete each sentence with the correct word from the word box.

1 The child asked her father to please _____ the seat on her old bicycle.

2 Our holiday dinners are special because my mother always makes a delicious

_____.

3 Our lazy cat loves to _____ by the window, napping in the sun.

4 The sun will always _____ in the eastern sky.

5 Emily asked her algebra teacher what _____ the failing grade would have on her average.

6 The _____ of the event could only be explained by saying a miracle had happened.

7 If you are ever lost in the _____, you should travel at night and sleep during the day.

8 John's mother asked him to _____ his backpack on his bed instead of on the couch.

9 Foolish campers sometimes _____ off the path, only to get lost or injured.

10 Psychologists often study how one patient's actions will _____ another patient.

Name _____ Date _____

Correct or Incorrect?

CONFUSING WORDS

Read each sentence. Circle **C** if the underlined word is used correctly. Circle **I** if the word is used incorrectly.

1 C I The medicine will have an immediate <u>affect</u> on her headache.

2 C I Scrapbooks are a nice way to remember the <u>past</u>.

3 C I The teachers and principal are part of the school <u>personnel</u>.

4 C I The lid on the milk container was <u>loose</u>.

5 C I We took a field trip to the <u>capital</u> building.

6 C I I will need to pay back the <u>loan</u> in thirty days.

7 C I <u>Accept</u> for my brother, my whole family wears glasses.

8 C I You must turn on the machine, and <u>then</u> push the button.

9 C I She was <u>conscious</u> of the noise in the background.

10 C I The sun <u>raises</u> each morning at 6:00 a.m.

11 C I I found the money <u>laying</u> in the street.

12 C I I read the <u>biography</u> of Abraham Lincoln.

13 C I The criminal <u>devised</u> a plan for escape.

14 C I How <u>good</u> do you know my uncle?

15 C I Can you <u>ensure</u> that we will all be safe?

16 C I We will have an <u>access</u> of thirty dollars after we pay our expenses.

17 C I I tell my best friend secrets because she is my <u>confident</u>.

18 C I I need to walk three blocks <u>farther</u> to reach my goal.

19 C I Some animals can learn to <u>adapt</u> to their surroundings.

20 C I Studying will definitely <u>effect</u> your grades.

Reading Skills • 7–8 © 2004 Creative Teaching Press

Finding Analogies

ANALOGIES

An **analogy** is a comparison between ideas. Analogies use ideas that are familiar to help explain unfamiliar ideas.
> **Example:**
> Breakfast is to morning as dinner is to evening.
> breakfast : morning :: dinner : evening

Notice that you can write an analogy in more than one way.

Read each analogy. Circle the choice that best completes the comparison.

1. square : box :: circle :   round   circle   sphere

2. chauffeur : car :: pilot :   airport   cockpit   jet

3. flower : stem :: tree :   leaf   trunk   root

4. bottom : top :: basement :   cellar   street   attic

5. mend : repair :: break :   destroy   burn   rip

6. December : winter :: September :   spring   month   autumn

7. fade : maid :: true :   false   new   honest

8. graceful : clumsy :: late :   morning   night   early

9. milk : beverage :: broccoli :   green   vegetable   bunch

10. puppy : dog :: child :   adult   boy   baby

Figure It Out

ANALOGIES

stationery	composite	stack
text	branch	teeth
mathematics	sanitary	brick
inventor	proud	flour

Complete each analogy with the correct word from the word box.

1 egg : omelet :: _____ : bread

2 author : _____ :: singer : lyrics

3 _____ : house :: fabric : clothing

4 ring : thing :: track : _____

5 Edison : _____ :: Columbus : explorer

6 _____ : clean :: frigid : cold

7 chemistry : science :: geometry : _____

8 whether : weather :: stationary : _____

9 leaf : _____ :: finger : hand

10 mice : mouse :: _____ : tooth

11 confident : arrogant :: _____ : haughty

12 three : prime :: twenty : _____

Write a sentence that includes a pair of words from above.

_____

_____

Analogy Puzzler

ANALOGIES

| bike | stir | theater | library |
| window | laugh | ink | doctor |

Complete each analogy with the correct word from the word box. Use the words to complete the crossword puzzle.

Across
2. car : metal :: _____ : glass
7. leg : man :: wheel : _____
8. key : house :: ticket : _____

Down
1. blender : mix :: spoon : _____
3. teacher : classroom :: _____ : hospital
4. painting : museum :: book : _____
5. lead : pencil :: _____ : pen
6. cry : sad :: _____ : happy

Reading Skills • 7-8 © 2004 Creative Teaching Press

Mind Challenge

ANALOGIES

Write the letter of the pair of words that best finishes each analogy.

1 stone : sculptor :: _____
  a. brick : house
  b. scalpel : surgeon
  c. mine : ore
  d. words : poet

2 ship : ocean :: _____
  a. store : magazine
  b. rocket : space
  c. water : faucet
  d. red : tomato

3 hair : Rapunzel :: _____
  a. lamp : Aladdin
  b. slipper : Cinderella
  c. nose : Pinochio
  d. rose : Beast

4 bread : oven :: _____
  a. pottery : kiln
  b. butter : churn
  c. ice : bucket
  d. vegetable : garden

5 adore : despise :: _____
  a. shovel : garden
  b. choose : reject
  c. water : ocean
  d. select : pick

6 emotion : love :: _____
  a. heart : feelings
  b. sadness : cry
  c. disease : measles
  d. car : truck

7 book : paper :: _____
  a. cheese : sandwich
  b. cabinet : wood
  c. writing : page
  d. computer : printer

8 comedian : funny :: _____
  a. fishing : patience
  b. surgeon : skilled
  c. artist : brushes
  d. singing : lovely

9 smart : genius :: _____
  a. intelligent : bright
  b. witty : cute
  c. silly : somber
  d. flexible : contortionist

10 thief : sneaky :: _____
  a. athlete : healthy
  b. day : tranquil
  c. prison : escape
  d. pain : aspirin

Reading Skills • 7–8 © 2004 Creative Teaching Press

Everyday Idioms

FIGURATIVE LANGUAGE

> **Idioms** are phrases that have a special meaning. The meaning is different from the usual or dictionary definition of the individual words.
>
> **Example:** Mrs. Rex has a green thumb.
>
> This phrase does not mean that Mrs. Rex's finger is the color green. The idiom *green thumb* means that she is a good gardener.

Read each description in Column A. Read each idiom in Column B. Write the letter of the idiom that matches each description.

Column A

Column B

1 _____ In a state of suspense or discomfort

a. Hit the books

2 _____ To be at risk of danger or trouble

b. Look down your nose

3 _____ To say something embarrassing

c. On pins and needles

4 _____ Divide playing cards

d. Drop me a line

5 _____ To study

e. Eat your words

6 _____ To help out

f. Lend a hand

7 _____ To call or write to someone

g. To be on thin ice

8 _____ Admit you were wrong

h. Bring down the house

9 _____ Please the audience with a good performance

i. Cut the deck

10 _____ Think other people are not as good as you

j. Put your foot in your mouth

Name _____ Date _____

Select a Simile

FIGURATIVE LANGUAGE

A **simile** is a figure of speech that compares two things and uses the word *like* or *as*.

Example:
Her eyes are as blue as the sea.

Complete each sentence by circling the letter of the simile that makes the best comparison.

1 Your feet are freezing. They're as
   a. sweet as sugar.
   b. cold as ice.
   c. white as snow.
   d. slow as a turtle.

2 Time moved slowly like
   a. a broken-down race car.
   b. a snail with no destination.
   c. a rabbit in the woods.
   d. the wind in a storm.

3 Our new house is tremendous. It's as
   a. spacious as a storybook castle.
   b. ancient as the hills.
   c. spooky as a haunted house.
   d. hard as stone.

4 The white, low-hanging moon was like
   a. an angry ball of fire.
   b. a threatening, dark cloud.
   c. a giant paper lantern in the sky.
   d. a fuzzy yellow tennis ball.

5 When I sneak up on my sister, I am
   a. as stealthy as a prowling cat.
   b. as loud as a thunderclap.
   c. very, very quiet.
   d. as dark as night.

6 The sunset was brilliant. The sky was
   a. like a dull gray blanket.
   b. as boring as yesterday's news.
   c. like seeing through a curtain.
   d. like a kaleidoscope of colors.

7 The lake was peaceful and quiet
   a. like a secret hideaway all my own.
   b. like the mall on a busy weekend.
   c. as the cafeteria at lunchtime.
   d. like the city waking up.

8 To Olympic athletes, winning a gold medal is
   a. like eating a big chocolate sundae.
   b. like climbing Mt. Everest.
   c. like riding a bicycle.
   d. an awesome prize.

22

Name _____ Date _____

  # Movie Metaphors

FIGURATIVE LANGUAGE

A **metaphor** compares two different things **without** using a word of comparison such as *like* or *as*.

Example: The snow was a silvery blanket on the grass.

Underline the metaphor in each movie review.

❶ The Long Night

This movie tells the story of a family trapped by a violent blizzard. The snowstorm is a fierce creature in this man vs. nature thriller. Snow falls in drifts as high as chimneys, testing the hero's resolve to fight for his family's survival. I think it deserves to be seen.

❷ A Sweet Song

In this movie, a piano player learns the sweetest songs ever written. The characters are very easy to like. Lisa, the pianist, has fingers that touch the keys as light and fast as raindrops. The music she plays is a powerful medicine that calms you instantly. A must-see!

❸ Flashback

This movie unsuccessfully combines action with science fiction. The story line swings from past to present like a pendulum, leaving the audience hopelessly confused. In addition to the characters being dull, the plot is a roller coaster of poorly related events. Pass on this "must not see."

❹ Sister Luck

A bright spot in the day, this movie makes you smile. A stubborn and resentful young girl learns that her disabled sister is a treasure to be cherished. The characters are likeable and true to life. I left feeling like I had been hugged.

Reading Skills • 7–8 © 2004 Creative Teaching Press

Name _____ Date _____

Identifying Figurative Language

FIGURATIVE LANGUAGE

Read each sentence. Circle **I** if the sentence contains an idiom, **S** if it contains a simile, or **M** if it contains a metaphor.

1   I   S   M   The girls put their heads together to find the answer.

2   I   S   M   Lend me your ear for a minute.

3   I   S   M   The clouds are like fluffy marshmallows in the sky.

4   I   S   M   Lisa is a songbird.

5   I   S   M   The skater was as graceful as a bird in flight.

6   I   S   M   The cat moved like a shadow in the night.

7   I   S   M   Dad's beard was a prickly porcupine.

8   I   S   M   If you don't hit the sheets, you won't get up on time.

9   I   S   M   Now that is a horse of a different color.

10   I   S   M   Her smile is like a shining star.

11   I   S   M   The full moon is a shiny balloon.

12   I   S   M   His feet were as big as boats.

13   I   S   M   Her hair is silk.

14   I   S   M   He appeared to be down in the dumps yesterday.

15   I   S   M   Brett was a fish at the swim meet on Saturday.

16   I   S   M   The boys are like two peas in a pod.

17   I   S   M   The giant's steps were thunder as he ran away.

18   I   S   M   It may cost an arm and a leg to get the car fixed.

19   I   S   M   The boy was as thin as a rail.

20   I   S   M   This class is like a three-ring circus.

Reading Skills • 7–8 © 2004 Creative Teaching Press

Name _____ Date _____

Homophones

HOMOPHONES AND HOMOGRAPHS

> **Homophones** are words that are pronounced the same but have different meanings and are spelled differently.
>
> **Examples:** ate, eight   to, too, two

Circle the homophone that correctly completes each sentence.

1 I wrote you a letter using my new (stationary, stationery).

2 The (principle, principal) at my school is Mrs. Reed.

3 She didn't know (weather, whether) to walk or run.

4 What color is (they're, their, there) car?

5 We found a (minor, miner) flaw in the painting.

6 He (threw, through) the baseball to the catcher.

7 In order to move (forward, foreword), we need to work together.

8 You can (lesson, lessen) the pressure in the tires by removing some air.

9 The doctor counted twenty (patients, patience) in the waiting room.

10 I placed my backpack (buy, bye, by) the computer.

11 We have won three championships in the (past, passed) five years.

12 What is the (capital, capitol) of Minnesota?

13 The farmer was going to (sheer, shear) the sheep.

14 The prisoner posted (bail, bale) to get out of jail.

15 My photograph has a (matte, mat) finish.

Reading Skills • 7–8 © 2004 Creative Teaching Press

Name _____ Date _____

Letter Home

HOMOPHONES AND HOMOGRAPHS

by, buy, bye	meet, meat	plane, plain	their, they're, there
eye, I	no, know	right, write	to, two, too
our, hour	sale, sail	weight, wait	sea, see
pear, pair, pare	would, wood	week, weak	ant, aunt
			hear, here

Complete the letter by filling in the blanks with the correct homophones.

Dear (1)_____ Meg,

    Last (2)_____ I went to visit my friend in California. I flew in a

(3)_____ and then drove for one (4)_____. My friend lives

(5)_____ the ocean. I had a chance to (6)_____ in her parents' new boat.

You (7)_____ love it! We even saw a (8)_____ of dolphins.

(9)_____ thought it was an amazing sight.

    After our boat trip, we decided to (10)_____ some people for lunch. We

didn't (11)_____ exactly where we were going. We walked for (12)_____

blocks before finding the restaurant. We were twenty minutes late, but luckily everyone

decided to (13)_____ for us. I had a wonderful time on my trip.

(14)_____ were so many exciting things to do and (15)_____. I couldn't

wait to (16)_____ and tell you all about it! I hope to (17)_____ from

you soon.

                 Love,
                 Terry

Reading Skills • 7–8 © 2004 Creative Teaching Press

Homographs

HOMOPHONES AND HOMOGRAPHS

Homographs are words that are spelled the same but have different meanings.

  Examples: saw   (1) a tool
                      (2) the past tense of "see"

Find two definitions in Column B for each homograph in column A. Write the letters of the definitions.

Column A

1. _____ swell
2. _____ record
3. _____ pitcher
4. _____ coat
5. _____ kind
6. _____ grave
7. _____ compact
8. _____ figure
9. _____ batter
10. _____ present
11. _____ desert
12. _____ refuse
13. _____ wind

Column B

a. a container that holds liquid
b. to put in writing
c. to pack together
d. considerate
e. to calculate
f. trash, garbage
g. great
h. one who hits
i. something on which sound is held
j. solid, dense
k. to cover
l. a hot, dry area of land
m. a burial plot
n. liquid cake mixture before baking
o. to grow or rise
p. shape
q. unwillingness to do something
r. a natural movement of air
s. clothing worn to keep warm
t. current, existing now
u. one who throws
v. a gift
w. very serious
x. category
y. to weave or entangle
z. to abandon

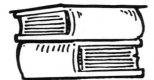

Homograph Logic

HOMOPHONES AND HOMOGRAPHS

trip	duck	wind	close
address	tear	refuse	saw
console	bear	fine	compress
store	sage	project	minute

Find the homograph that relates to both words in each pair. Write it on the line.

1 shut _____ near

2 speech _____ home

3 comfort _____ controls

4 squeeze _____ bandage

5 turn _____ air

6 cower _____ bird

7 cut _____ seen

8 okay _____ penalty

9 rip _____ cry

10 carry _____ mammal

11 tiny _____ time

12 activity _____ throw

13 wise _____ herb

14 business _____ hold

15 reject _____ garbage

16 fall _____ vacation

Reading Skills • 7–8 © 2004 Creative Teaching Press

Conquering Context Clues

CONTEXT CLUES

You can use the familiar words in a sentence to figure out the meaning of a word you don't recognize. This is called using **context clues**.

Circle the word that has the same meaning as the underlined word.

1 My grandmother lives on a farm and loves the <u>rural</u> life.

    country   busy   relaxing

2 I felt a little <u>apprehensive</u> the first time I traveled alone.

    tired   confident   worried

3 After our busy day, the warm room made me feel <u>drowsy</u>.

    scared   sleepy   happy

4 I was <u>intrigued</u> by the book and wanted to learn more.

    interested   bored   angered

5 The mother horse kept close watch over her <u>foal</u>.

    baby   food   shelter

6 The <u>buffet</u> was filled with many kinds of meat, salads, and desserts.

    car   fancy collar   food line

7 The dinner guests were disappointed at the <u>meager</u> portions of food on their plates.

    puny   generous   delicious

8 The performance was live, so when the actor forgot his lines, he had to <u>improvise</u>.

    remember   laugh   make up something

9 <u>Repercussions</u> of the terrible accident were felt even weeks after it happened.

    effects   drums   crying

10 All our <u>kin</u>, including 100-year-old Aunt Fern, attended my parents' 50th wedding anniversary party.

    friends   neighbors   relatives

Reading Skills • 7–8 © 2004 Creative Teaching Press

Meaning Sleuth

CONTEXT CLUES

Sometimes you can find clues that will help you decipher unknown words. Look for synonyms or antonyms around the unknown word.

Read each set of sentences. Use context clues to determine the correct meaning of the underlined word. Circle the letter of the word that has the same meaning.

1 My brother has an <u>antiquated</u> computer. It still uses a disk drive, and it is older than I am.
   a. old
   b. new
   c. modern
   d. small

2 The leader was <u>revered</u> for her charity work. She gave many hours of her own time to help others, and people admired her for it.
   a. disliked
   b. concerned
   c. respected
   d. criticized

3 The teacher did not believe the student's dog destroyed his homework. She called his parents to see if they would give <u>credence</u> to his story.
   a. laughter
   b. believability
   c. anger
   d. examples

4 The crime was <u>premeditated</u>. The thieves thought out every detail before actually committing the robbery.
   a. surprising
   b. accidental
   c. disorganized
   d. planned

5 Finishing the project was a <u>daunting</u> task. It would not be easy to meet such a tight deadline.
   a. simple
   b. difficult
   c. small
   d. strange

6 The <u>errant</u> pitch almost hit a fan who was sitting in the front row.
   a. straight
   b. centered
   c. strange
   d. off-course

Reading Skills • 7–8 © 2004 Creative Teaching Press

Name _____ Date _____

Reading for Clues

CONTEXT CLUES

Read the paragraph. Then circle the letter of the best answer for each question.

Ben Franklin was a <u>remarkable</u> man. He began his career as an <u>apprentice</u>, or student, in a print shop. He <u>excelled</u> in this field and soon began publishing a newspaper. He also published an advice book called *Poor Richard's Almanack*. After tiring of the publishing business, Franklin built a career as a scientist. He was a <u>prolific</u> inventor and was rarely idle. He experimented with electricity, and invented many things, including bifocal glasses. Later in his life, Franklin became a <u>diplomat</u>. His ability to help nations work through their problems gained him worldwide recognition. Franklin is considered one of America's <u>founding fathers</u>, helping to create a new nation. He will always be remembered for his many talents.

1 Based on this paragraph, <u>remarkable</u> means
    a. lazy.
    b. confused.
    c. proper.
    d. impressive.

2 You can figure out that <u>excelled</u> means "did well" because
    a. he went on to publish a newspaper.
    b. he became an inventor.
    c. he was a student.
    d. he created bifocal glasses.

3 An <u>apprentice</u> is
    a. an inventor.
    b. a student.
    c. a scientist.
    d. a publisher.

4 Someone who is <u>prolific</u> would be
    a. average.
    b. dangerous.
    c. common.
    d. productive.

5 The main job of a <u>diplomat</u> is to
    a. help nations get along.
    b. teach college classes.
    c. write novels.
    d. invent devices to help people.

6 <u>Founding fathers</u> are best described as
    a. new fathers.
    b. creators of a nation.
    c. foreign leaders.
    d. entertainers.

Name _____ Date _____

 # Dictionary Detective
Context Clues

Read each dictionary entry. Then read each sentence and decide which definition of the word is meant. Write the number of the correct definition.

| extract: | **a.** to draw or pull out |
| | **b.** a product such as a juice made by withdrawing from a source |

1 The dentist needed to <u>extract</u> the bad tooth. _____

2 I used vanilla <u>extract</u> in the recipe. _____

monitor:	**a.** a student assistant
	b. a screen used for viewing
	c. to check or test

3 Mr. Henderson will <u>monitor</u> our progress on the project. _____

4 I'm having trouble with the <u>monitor</u> on my computer. _____

draft:	**a.** the act of drawing
	b. the selection of a person for military service
	c. a current of air
	d. an early sketch, outline, or version

5 Marta finished the rough <u>draft</u> of her paper. _____

6 The architect will <u>draft</u> the blueprints of our house. _____

7 Please shut the window to keep out the <u>draft</u>. _____

taste:	**a.** to try or determine flavor
	b. a small amount
	c. individual preference
	d. experience

8 I just want a <u>taste</u> of the chocolate cake. _____

9 My decorating <u>taste</u> is quite different from my brother's. _____

10 Tim wanted to get a <u>taste</u> of college life. _____

Reading Skills • 7–8 © 2004 Creative Teaching Press

Name _____ Date _____

Human Body Classification

CLASSIFYING EVENTS AND IDEAS

Classifying is grouping items according to their shared characteristics. Classifying information helps you select and organize details, allowing for easy reference and memory retention.

Below is a list of five systems of the human body and some of their parts, but the list is out of order. Write each word in its proper place on the following organizational chart.

intestines	biceps	digestive	lungs	heart
blood	muscular	ribs	nose	collarbone
deltoids	stomach	respiratory	circulatory	skeletal

System	Parts
_____	_____ _____
_____	_____ _____
_____	_____ _____
_____	_____ _____
_____	_____ _____

Reading Skills • 7–8 © 2004 Creative Teaching Press

Name _____ Date _____

Classify Details

CLASSIFYING EVENTS AND IDEAS

The following notes are for a persuasive paper on the importance of keeping a local park clean. Write each detail in its proper place on the organizational chart.

Details
dangerous to children; littered; organize a cleanup crew; dirty water; animals could be harmed; pick up our own garbage; clean graffiti; beautiful to look at; safe place to play; broken glass

Current situation:	_____ _____ _____ _____ _____
How we can help:	_____ _____ _____ _____ _____
Benefits of a clean park:	_____ _____ _____ _____ _____

Name _____ Date _____

 # Classified Ads

CLASSIFYING EVENTS AND IDEAS

Look at the classified advertisements for summer jobs. Use them to answer the questions that follow.

Lifeguard
Fri., Sat., Sun., 1–9 p.m.
Must have first aid training.
$10.00/hr. to start.
Apply in person: Turner Pool

Babysitter
Mon.–Fri., 4–6 p.m.
Care for 3 children, ages 3–8.
First aid training is a must.
Call 555–0110.

Library Assistant
Tues. and Thurs. mornings.
$6.50/hr. No prior experience
necessary. Call 555–1111 for
an interview.

Summer Only—Cleaning Crew
Looking for hard-working people
to assist in cleaning the middle
school. No experience necessary.
Mon.–Thurs., 9–11 a.m.
No phone calls, please. Interviews
at school Fri. and Sat., 1–5 p.m.

Wilson's Donut Shop
Tues.–Sat. Baker's assistant needed
6–9 a.m. Basic cooking skills
required. Phone 555-2222, or come
in for an interview.

1 Which jobs do not require experience?

_____

_____

2 Which jobs have evening hours?

_____

_____

3 Which jobs require training in first aid?

_____

_____

4 Which jobs will accept phone inquiries?

_____

_____

_____

5 Which jobs include the pay rate?

_____

_____

6 Only one job gives you a Tuesday off. Which one?

_____

Reading Skills • 7–8 © 2004 Creative Teaching Press

Name _____ Date _____

Classifying History

CLASSIFYING EVENTS AND IDEAS

Write each fact under the president that it describes. Hint: Some facts may apply to more than one president.

Gettysburg Address   was a general
was assassinated   ended slavery
youngest president   sparked space exploration
first president   bought the Louisiana Purchase
wrote the Declaration of Independence the tallest president

Washington	Lincoln

Jefferson	Kennedy

Story Ordering

SEQUENCING

Sequencing means arranging things in a logical order. For a story, that order is often chronological, or time order.

Read each story idea and the details that follow it. Number the details in the proper sequence.

1 Jefferson Middle School put on a dinner theatre night for students and parents.
_____ The students sold tickets to "Murder Mystery at Blaylock Inn."
_____ Dinner theatre night was a complete success.
_____ Since the event was set for Halloween weekend, the students planned the performance, decorations, and menu accordingly.
_____ The home economics and drama teachers decided on a date for the event.
_____ The home economics class started food preparation while the dress rehearsal took place.

2 Fascinated with hummingbirds, Amy planned and tended a garden to attract them.
_____ She watered the garden daily and waited impatiently for a tiny, winged visitor.
_____ Amy researched what to plant and how to care for plants that attract hummingbirds.
_____ She planted bugle-shaped flowers like honeysuckle and petunias.
_____ Amy described in a journal the type and behavior of the hummingbird she had seen.
_____ Amy watched quietly and smiled to herself as a jewel-colored hummingbird sipped nectar from the flowers.

3 William gets an after-school job to earn spending money.
_____ He dressed with care to meet Mr. Conner, the hardware store manager.
_____ William was never able to go places with his buddies because his family had no money for entertainment.
_____ Mr. Conner hired William to stock shelves and keep them neat and organized.
_____ William went to the movies with his buddies and stuffed himself with snacks and sodas, just because he could. He felt sick and happy at the same time.
_____ William found a classified ad for a hardware store looking for a stock boy.

Note Card Mix-Up

Sequencing

Mike dropped the note cards he had prepared for his speech about the life of Anne Frank. Number the cards in the proper sequence.

The Gestapo left Anne's diary behind, believing the papers were unimportant.

After the war, Anne's diary was given to Otto Frank, the only survivor of the family.

Her family was discovered and arrested.

Anne Frank was born June 12, 1929, in Frankfurt, Germany.

Anne died from typhus in Bergen-Belsen, a German concentration camp.

Anne was a bright student, but she was forced to leave her school to attend a Jewish school.

Anne and her family moved into their secret hiding place to escape the Gestapo.

In her diary, Anne wrote her deepest thoughts and keen observations about the others in hiding with her.

Name _____ Date _____

What's the Order?

SEQUENCING

Read the passage, which describes how to repot a plant.

Repotting a plant that has grown too large for its container is important. First, you will need to purchase a pot that is two times larger than the base of the plant. Check this carefully. Then purchase potting soil and peat moss. Mix the two together in a wheelbarrow, and fill the new container halfway with the mixture. Carefully move the plant from the old pot into the new one. Fill the pot to the top with the remaining mixture, and then water it.

What are the steps for repotting a plant? Number the steps in the proper sequence.

_____ Buy potting soil and peat moss.

_____ Water the plant.

_____ Mix the potting soil with peat moss.

_____ Purchase a new pot.

_____ Move the plant from the old pot to the new one.

_____ Fill the pot to the top with the soil mixture.

_____ Put half of the soil mixture into the pot.

Order the Steps

Sequencing

Read the passage, which describes how to make an egg float.

Would you believe that you could make an egg float? Amaze your friends and family with this science trick. Fill a container about half full with warm water. Next, stir in some salt. Continue to stir and add salt until it no longer dissolves, but sits on the bottom of the container. Leave the mixture to settle for a few hours. Then carefully pour off the clear liquid into a glass jar or jug, leaving the salt that didn't dissolve behind. Now comes the fun part! Show your friends the normal egg and ask if they think you can make it float. Carefully drop the egg into the salt water and watch their amazement as your egg bobs on the top of the water. The egg will float, even if you push it down.

Number the steps in the proper sequence.

_____ Continue adding salt and stirring until it no longer dissolves.

_____ Carefully drop the egg into the water.

_____ Fill a container half full with warm water.

_____ Push the egg under water to see what happens.

_____ Leave the mixture to settle.

_____ Pour off the clear liquid into a glass jar or jug.

_____ Add salt to the water.

Reading Skills • 7–8 © 2004 Creative Teaching Press

Name _____ Date _____

Brownie Recipe

FOLLOWING DIRECTIONS

Use the recipe directions to answer the questions.

Mom's Brownies

Brownies

3 eggs   1 cup flour
1½ cups oil   1 tsp. baking soda
½ cup sugar   1 tsp. salt
½ cup cocoa   nuts (optional)

In a large bowl, mix eggs, oil, and sugar until well blended. Add cocoa and continue to stir until the batter is smooth. In a separate bowl, sift together flour, baking soda, and salt. Then slowly add the flour mixture to the cocoa mixture. Beat by hand 75–80 times. Some lumps may remain. If adding nuts, do so at this time. Pour mixture into a greased 9 x 13 inch pan. Bake at 350° for 45 minutes. Serve warm or cooled.

1 How many bowls do you need to make this recipe? _____

2 Number the steps in the correct order.

_____ Beat mixture by hand 75–80 times.

_____ Pour into a greased pan.

_____ Add nuts, if desired.

_____ Sift flour, baking soda, and salt.

_____ Add cocoa.

_____ Mix eggs, oil, and sugar.

3 Which step is optional? _____

4 At what temperature should you bake the brownies? _____

5 How long should the brownies bake? _____

Name _____   Date _____

Using a Flowchart
FOLLOWING DIRECTIONS

Use the flowchart to answer the questions.

What to Do When You Are Sick

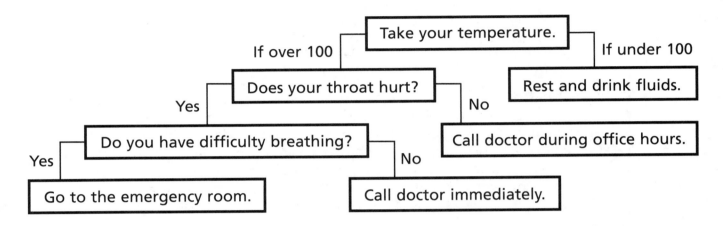

1 What is the first thing you should do when you are sick?

_____

2 What should you do if your throat does NOT hurt?

_____

3 Should you go to the doctor if your temperature is under 100?

_____

4 What should you do if you have difficulty breathing?

_____

5 What are the symptoms you have if you should call the doctor immediately?

_____

_____

Reading Skills • 7–8 © 2004 Creative Teaching Press

Map It!

FOLLOWING DIRECTIONS

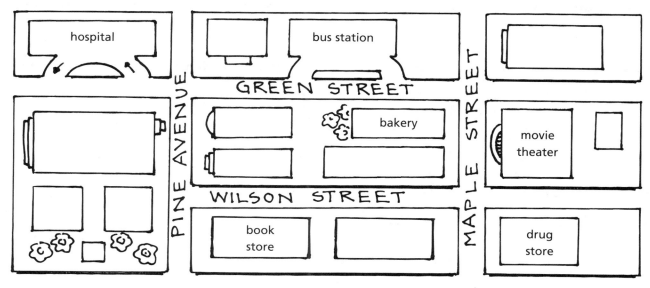

Read each statement. Use the information to write the name of each place in its correct location on the map.

1 The *music store* is next to the bakery on the corner of Green Street and Pine Avenue.

2 The *bank* is across the street from the music store and next to the bus station.

3 The *school* is across the street from the hospital.

4 There is a *parking lot* next to the bus station.

5 The *tennis court* is next to the school near Pine Avenue.

6 There is a *popcorn stand* behind the movie theater.

7 The *police station* is across from the bakery, on Wilson Street.

8 The *playground* is next to the school.

9 There is a *drinking fountain* near the trees.

10 The *library* is across the street from the movie theater.

11 The *coffee shop* is next to the book store and across the street from the drug store.

12 The *hotel* is on the corner of Wilson Street and Pine Avenue.

Reading Skills • 7–8 © 2004 Creative Teaching Press

Name _____ Date _____

Code Breaker

FOLLOWING DIRECTIONS

> Thx xlqrxt tol suqqxs li zay qlosx lattxnti to thx dxltail and nxvxr giv luz.

Break the secret code by following each step in order. Use the lines below to work out each clue. Write your final answer on the line at the bottom of the page.

1 Change all the **x**'s to **e**'s.

2 Cross out all the **l**'s except for the fourth and seventh ones.

3 Add an **s** to the beginning of the second word.

4 Add **ing** to the end of the sixth and fourteenth words.

5 Change the **q**'s to **c**'s.

6 Change the **z**'s to **p**'s.

7 Add **on** to the end of the eighth word.

8 Add an **s** to the end of the fourth, fifth, and eleventh words.

_____

_____

_____

_____

_____

_____

_____

The unscrambled sentence says:

_____

Reading Skills • 7–8 © 2004 Creative Teaching Press

Name _____ Date _____

Find the Cause or Effect

CAUSE AND EFFECT

Read each selection. Fill in the cause and effect boxes.

Harriet Tubman was a strong, determined woman born into the injustice of slavery. She became an important link in the Underground Railroad, guiding runaway slaves to freedom in the North. If she were to be caught doing this, it meant certain death. Despite grave danger, she returned time and again to help free more slaves.

Cause	**Effect**
1. _____	Runaway slaves escaped to freedom.
2. _____	
3. _____	

Though Thomas Edison had many failures in his career as an inventor, we will never know about them. He used each failure as a stepping stone, making adjustments until he was successful. Edison was a prolific inventor whose persistence resulted in many modern conveniences. He is credited with over 1,000 inventions, including the light bulb and the motion picture camera.

Cause	**Effect**
Edison was extremely persistent.	4. _____
	5. _____

Susan B. Anthony was determined to win the right to vote for all women in America. She traveled throughout the country speaking about equal rights and inspiring others to join the fight. She voted in Rochester, NY and was arrested for it. Susan B. Anthony became president of the National American Woman Suffrage Association in 1892. She died in 1906 and never saw her dream become reality. It wasn't until 1920 that the Nineteenth Amendment was established, giving women the right to vote. It is also referred to as the Susan B. Anthony Amendment.

Cause	**Effect**
6. _____	7. _____
8. _____	9. _____

Name _____ Date _____

Just Because

Cause and Effect

Read each set of effects. Circle the letter of the most likely cause.

1 Amy's phone and television were taken away from her and she had to come straight home from school.
   a. She earned a reward.
   b. She was grounded.
   c. She had to babysit her little brother.
   d. She was really angry.

2 Cole won first place in the district speech competition.
   a. He improvised his speech at the competition.
   b. His competitors were not prepared.
   c. He chose a strong topic and held the judges' attention.
   d. He was so nervous his voice trembled.

3 Billy called his mother from school and begged her to bring him his book report.
   a. Billy was scatter-brained.
   b. He was not finished with his report.
   c. The report was due that day.
   d. He never forgot his homework.

4 The letters on the board looked fuzzy to Terry and he always had a headache after school.
   a. Terry did not like to read.
   b. He was sickly and always complaining.
   c. Terry probably needed eyeglasses.
   d. Terry could not read.

5 Sheila didn't know any answers on the test. She had a funny feeling in her stomach. All she could think about was the movie that she had stayed up late to watch.
   a. Sheila was well rested.
   b. Sheila worked hard preparing for her test.
   c. Sheila had a bad cold.
   d. Sheila didn't study for her test.

6 Campers and wildlife ran to safety. The night sky glowed an eerie orange. Overpowering fumes filled the air.
   a. Someone's house caught fire.
   b. A forest fire was spreading rapidly.
   c. The firemen put the fire out.
   d. Everyone was rescued.

Reading Skills • 7–8 © 2004 Creative Teaching Press

Frederick Douglass

CAUSE AND EFFECT

The story of Frederick Bailey's life is one of bitterness and triumph, struggles and successes. He was born into slavery on a plantation in Maryland and was kept ignorant of his birth date and his father's identity. He knew only that his mother was a slave who was sent away from him and that his father was a white man.

As a boy in Baltimore, his master's wife began teaching him to read, but she stopped when her husband found out about it. He said that educating a slave was not only unlawful, but would make the boy unfit to be a slave any longer. Frederick overheard his words and knew from that moment on education was his key to freedom. He began to trick poor white boys in the neighborhood into giving him small reading lessons, betting them for bread that he could read better than they could.

After many years of bondage, serving not only as a house servant in the city, but also as a hard-laboring field hand on the plantation, Frederick finally escaped to freedom in New York and married Anna Murray. They settled in New Bedford, Massachusetts where he changed his name to Frederick Douglass to avoid being found by those who would return him to slavery. It was there that he was first encouraged to tell of his enslavement. Douglass became instrumental in advancing the abolitionist movement, the struggle to end slavery, because of his ability to capture an audience with his words and emotion. He eventually published a newspaper called the *North Star*. It was dedicated to exposing the horrors of slavery. He served as an advisor to President Lincoln during the Civil War and recruited black men into the Union Army.

Read the passage about Frederick Douglass. Then answer the questions.

1 Frederick knew education would be his key to success because
- **a.** he liked to be difficult.
- **b.** he heard his master say educating him would make him unfit to be a slave.
- **c.** learning was hard and took a long time.
- **d.** his successful father was an educated man.

2 Because it was unlawful to teach slaves to read, Frederick
- **a.** gave up trying to learn.
- **b.** begged his mistress to teach him anyway.
- **c.** learned completely on his own.
- **d.** cleverly tricked others into teaching him.

3 List three things Douglass did to help further the abolitionist movement.

_____

_____

_____

Name _____ Date _____

The American Revolution

CAUSE AND EFFECT

The American Revolution was a war in which the colonies fought to gain their independence from Britain. Many events led up to the decision to go to war.

The King and Parliament made laws for the colonies and sent governors to enact them. Many of these laws included taxes which the colonists were forced to pay. The Sugar Act of 1764 was one that caused great concern. This act required colonists to pay tax on everyday items like sugar, textiles, coffee, and dye. Many people felt this was an unfair law.

Later that same year, England passed the Currency Act. This law prevented colonies from making their own money. People in the colonies began to talk openly about the unfairness of the laws. They wanted to have some say in the laws that were made for them. They demanded an end to taxation without representation. Unfortunately, England ignored their demands. In fact, things only got worse.

In 1765, the Stamp Act was passed. This law enacted a tax on all printed material, including documents, newspapers, bills, pamphlets, and even playing cards! One of the final blows to colonists was the passing of the Tea Act, which was an attempt to save Britain's East India Company from bankruptcy. It allowed the company to sell tea directly to the colonists without paying the regular taxes. Therefore, they could sell it much cheaper. American merchants felt the threat of a British monopoly. This law sparked a great colonial rebellion known as the Boston Tea Party. Groups of colonists began meeting secretly to oppose British rule. After being ignored by the King and Parliament, the colonists decided to make a stand. They refused to allow Britain to impose laws that restricted their trade and limited their freedom. Each new action by Parliament brought the colonies closer together and further down the road to revolution.

Read the passage about the American Revolution. Then answer the questions.

 1 All of the following are causes of the American Revolution <u>except</u>
- a. taxation without representation.
- b. Parliament ignoring the colonists' demands.
- c. the King's refusal to visit the colonies.
- d. laws like the Stamp Act and the Sugar Act.

 2 The Boston Tea Party was a response to
- a. a tax put on newspapers.
- b. a tax put on sugar and coffee.
- c. the law forbidding colonists to print money.
- d. the threat of a British monopoly.

 3 According to the passage, what law prompted colonists to speak openly about the unfairness of England?

_____

Reading Skills • 7–8 © 2004 Creative Teaching Press

Inference Practice

MAKING INFERENCES

> **Inferences** are judgements you make when the author gives you clues, but does not give you the information directly.

Read each situation. Answer the questions.

1 Sarah and Dylan had been looking forward to their beach vacation for weeks. Their family drove straight to the shoreline so they could be sure to have the whole day for swimming. When they arrived, Sarah and Dylan pretended not to notice the dark gray sky. They jumped out of the car and ran toward the water. Their parents looked on, surprised when their children turned around and dove back into the car, wrapping themselves in towels.

What inference can you make?
   a. Sarah and her brother had a fight.
   b. The hotel was closed for the weekend.
   c. The weather was too cold to swim.
   d. Sarah's dad had arrived at the wrong hotel.

2 The Student Council organized a food drive competition with other schools in the area. The challenge was for each school to collect as many cans of food as possible to donate to a local food pantry. The school that collected the most cans would win a free concert in the park with a famous band. A second warehouse has been opened to hold all the cans collected in the first two weeks.

What can you infer about the food drive?
   a. Students are not interested in the project.
   b. Students are motivated by the reward.
   c. The project will not be successful.
   d. The Student Council will cancel the concert.

3 Michael loves to play baseball. He spends his weekends on the field or training with his coach. He went to baseball camp and received special instruction from a professional pitcher. He lives, eats, and sleeps baseball!

Which of these sentences is probably true?
   a. Michael is not a hard worker.
   b. Basketball is very important to Michael.
   c. Michael's parents do not support his goals.
   d. Michael wants to be a professional baseball player.

Name _____ Date _____

What a Character!

MAKING INFERENCES

Read each character description. Answer the questions.

1 Maria was walking home from school. When she reached the corner, she noticed something on the ground under the bush. She looked more closely and saw a purse. She looked inside to see if there was a name or address. She noticed a very large amount of money. Maria quickly closed the purse and took it to the grocery store near the corner. She gave the purse to the grocer who promised to call the owner.
What can you infer about Maria?

    a. Maria didn't need the money.
    b. Maria cannot be trusted
    c. Maria is an honest person.
    d. Maria usually rides the bus home.

2 Mr. Adams gives a lot of homework. He grades papers quickly and returns them with comments. He gives tardy slips if you are even one minute late to his class. He knows the names of every student's mom and dad. He expects full participation in his classes. He listens to every student's answers, no matter how long.
What inference can you make about Mr. Adams?

    a. Mr. Adams is a mean teacher.
    b. Mr. Adams does not like his job.
    c. Mr. Adams' class is easy.
    d. Mr. Adams is a dedicated teacher.

3 Sophia wanted to be friends with a group of popular girls in her school. She often sat near them, hoping they would notice her. One day, they began a conversation and included her. She was excited to join in. They were telling jokes and making fun of some of the other girls in their class. When they looked to Sophia for her opinion, she felt uncomfortable. After a few minutes, Sophia excused herself and went to talk with someone else.
Which of these sentences is probably true?

    a. Sophia will continue to want to be friends with the girls.
    b. Sophia will find other friends who are more kind.
    c. Sophia will talk badly about the popular girls.
    d. Sophia will never have any friends.

Reading Skills • 7–8 © 2004 Creative Teaching Press

What's Happening?

MAKING INFERENCES

Read each scenario. Make inferences to determine what event is being described.

1 The woman held her breath as she watched her 10-month-old child let go of the coffee table and balance on his tiny unsure feet one at a time. When he fell into her arms, she hoisted him in the air, exclaiming, "You did it!"

_____

2 The audience was visibly saddened and distressed. They thought that the Civil War would never last so long or cause so much death and destruction. The tall, somber president with the beard and top hat stood to address the crowd. "Four score and seven years ago . . ."

_____

3 The self-conscious young girl who usually refused to smile was all grins this morning. After 18 months of keeping a straight face and talking as little as possible, she was finally free! It was like a floodgate had been opened. She wanted to talk to everyone and have them notice her new smile.

_____

4 A dark-skinned, tired woman climbed onto the bus and found a seat. At the next stop, more people boarded and some were left standing in the aisle. All eyes were on the lady and silent tension filled the air. I'm not giving up my seat for anyone, she thought. I have a right to sit here just like any of them.

_____

5 Excited and nervous, Jay got behind the wheel of his father's car. A serious-looking man with a clipboard and pen climbed into the passenger seat next to him. When the man nodded, Jay started the car and carefully pulled away from the curb. He thought to himself, I hope he doesn't make me parallel park.

_____

Infer the Meaning

MAKING INFERENCES

Read each description. Make inferences to answer the questions.

1 A gentleman from the city purchased camping supplies he needed from the general store out by the mountains. He looked confused when the old clerk drawled, "That foots up $10.89."
"Foots up" must mean
   a. his foot is up.
   b. adds up to be.
   c. lots of money.
   d. discounts.

2 Though natural enemies, the kitten and crow developed a fascinating amity. They would wrestle together, sit on the fence together, and eat together. Never did they fight or fear one another.
"Amity" must mean
   a. enemies.
   b. language.
   c. feeling.
   d. friendship.

3 Thomas Edison was a man credited with over 1,000 inventions in his lifetime. He remarked once that genius is one percent inspiration and ninety-nine percent perspiration.
What can you infer was his belief?
   a. A good idea is all you need to be successful.
   b. He considered himself a genius.
   c. Successful men are born that way.
   d. It takes hard work to turn a good idea into reality.

4 Louisa worked hard all her life. As a child, she never got to go to school because her family needed her to work. Now, her children, grandchildren, and her brother's family all live in her house. She feels rich because she bought that house with her hard-earned money. She has the papers to prove it. Her daughter read them to her the day she moved in.
What can you infer about Louisa?
   a. Louisa is a sad woman.
   b. Her family does not appreciate her.
   c. Louisa never learned to read.
   d. Louisa resents having to work so hard.

Reading Skills • 7–8 © 2004 Creative Teaching Press

Which Is Which?

FACT AND OPINION

Facts are things that can be proven true. **Opinions** tell how people feel or think about something. They may or may not be true.

Fact: Red is a primary color.
Opinion: Red is the best color for a kitchen.

Circle **F** if the statement is a fact. Circle **O** if the statement is an opinion.

1. F O Sometimes the month of February has 29 days.

2. F O Children should never wear dark colors at night.

3. F O Truck exhaust contributes to pollution.

4. F O Listening to music is a great way to relax.

5. F O Grape is not a good flavor for drinks.

6. F O Artists are very temperamental.

7. F O Golden retrievers are often trained as rescue dogs.

8. F O The piano is a percussion instrument.

9. F O Every house should have fresh flowers in the kitchen.

10. F O Washington, D.C. is the capital of the United States.

11. F O Poor dental hygiene leads to cavities.

12. F O Fruits and vegetables are part of a healthy diet.

13. F O People with brown hair are more outgoing.

14. F O Animal lovers have kind hearts.

15. F O Reading and math are the most important subjects.

16. F O The Bill of Rights is an addition to the U.S. Constitution.

17. F O We must have oxygen to survive.

Identifying Fact and Opinion

FACT AND OPINION

Read each passage. Answer the questions.

1 The Wilmington Flyers have a winning record this season. Their fans are the best in baseball. Over 10,000 people attended Thursday's game. The final score was 7–2. Which statement is an opinion?

    a. The Wilmington Flyers have a winning record this season.
    b. Their fans are the best in baseball.
    c. Over 10,000 people attended Thursday's game.
    d. The final score was 7–2.

2 The winter season is great. Sports like sledding and skiing are done in snowy climates. Cold weather makes you feel alive. All people should experience the brisk feel of winter!
Which statement is a fact?

    a. The winter season is great.
    b. Sports like sledding and skiing are done in snowy climates.
    c. Cold weather makes you feel alive.
    d. All people should experience the brisk feel of winter!

3 A balanced diet includes many types of food. Apples should be something everyone eats. Broccoli has a strong, somewhat unpleasant taste. Blueberries have the best taste. They should be included in every meal.
Which statement is a fact?

    a. A balanced diet includes many types of food.
    b. Broccoli has a strong, somewhat unpleasant taste.
    c. Blueberries have the best taste.
    d. They should be included in every meal.

4 There's no doubt that Friday is the best day of the week. That's the day the high school football games take place. Everyone loves bundling up in warm clothes to watch the game. Cheering on your favorite team is always fun.
Which statement is a fact?

    a. There's no doubt that Friday is the best day of the week.
    b. That's the day the high school football games take place.
    c. Everyone loves bundling up in warm clothes to watch the game.
    d. Cheering on your favorite team is always fun.

Reading Skills • 7–8 © 2004 Creative Teaching Press

Sorting Facts and Opinions

FACT AND OPINION

Read each topic sentence. Then read the supporting details. Determine which details are facts and which are opinions. Write the letter of each detail in the matching column.

1 **Topic Sentence:** The World's Fair was held in Chicago in 1893.

   a. The World's Fair was also known as the Columbian Exposition.
   b. The Ferris wheel was introduced at the fair.
   c. The fair was far superior to the one held in France several years earlier.
   d. People who attended felt it was beyond compare.
   e. There were more than 25,000,000 admissions to the fair.
   f. The fair's midway was noisy and distracting.

Facts		**Opinions**
_____		_____
_____		_____

2 **Topic Sentence:** The design of zoos has changed greatly in the past 100 years.

   a. Many zoos have designed natural habitat exhibits for their animals.
   b. Children enjoy zoos more than adults.
   c. Natural habitat zoos are more interesting to visit.
   d. Some people protested keeping animals in cages.
   e. Zoos have saved some animals from extinction.
   f. In the past, animals were displayed in cages.

Facts		**Opinions**
_____		_____
_____		_____
_____		_____

Name _____ Date _____

 # Analyze an Editorial

FACT AND OPINION

The Value of a Park or a Parking Lot

The city of Franklin is planning to build a parking lot over Willow Park. They believe that business in the downtown area will grow if a parking lot is nearby. Officials stated that the park provides little value to citizens of this town. I completely disagree and so do many others.

Willow Park was the first park built in Franklin. It will be 100 years old this spring. I believe that nearly every person in this town has run, played, sat, or picnicked there at some point. The beautiful tree-lined space gives our city charm. The town would suffer if it were no longer a part of our community.

Besides the history of the park, it also serves many purposes. People walk their dogs in the park. Children play in the park while their parents are shopping. Many businesspeople love to eat their lunch there on spring days.

The park also contains twenty-four flower boxes. Over 12,000 flowers are planted in them each spring. Everyone loves these floral displays, which make the downtown space look beautiful all summer long. No one will stop to enjoy the beauty of a concrete parking lot!

Willow Park is a part of our history. It should remain a part of our present and future. Make your voice heard. A petition will be available for signing outside city hall. A meeting will be held on Saturday at 10:00 a.m. Join our fight to save the park. You won't be sorry that you did!

Read the editorial. Answer the questions.

1 Which of the following is an opinion of city officials?
    a. Willow Park is important for citizens.
    b. A parking lot will improve downtown business.
    c. Willow Park is in Franklin.
    d. None of the above

2 Which of these statements from the editorial is a fact?
    a. You won't be sorry that you did.
    b. The park also contains twenty-four flower boxes.
    c. No one will stop to enjoy the beauty of a concrete parking lot.
    d. These floral displays make the downtown space look beautiful all summer long.

3 Which statement is an opinion of the author?
    a. People walk their dogs in the park.
    b. The park will be 100 years old this spring.
    c. Over 12,000 flowers are planted in them each spring.
    d. The town would suffer if the park were no longer a part of this community.

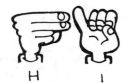

Story Summary

SUMMARIZING

Helen Keller was born in 1880 in Tuscumbia, Alabama. An illness robbed her of her hearing and sight while she was still a baby. She grew to be a very difficult and determined child, locked in her own darkness, and spoiled by those who loved her because they could not communicate with her. She took food from others' plates at the dinner table, and she would kick or scratch people when she was angry. No one knew how to help her.

Finally, Miss Annie Sullivan, who was a graduate of the Perkins Institute for the Blind, came to live with the family to be Helen's governess. Fortunately for Helen, Annie matched her own determination in every way. Annie taught Helen to finger spell words in her hand. Helen learned the signs quickly, but she did not know what they meant, or that they even had meaning at all. Helen continued her temper tantrums when she did not get her way, and Annie tirelessly fought to change her horrible behavior and bring Helen out of her isolated world.

Then one miraculous day at the pump house, Helen finally made the connection that each finger spelling had meaning. She felt the water coming out of the pump while Annie spelled the word in her hand. At that moment, she understood that everything had a name and that she could relate to the world in a whole new way. She became an eager student whose perseverance will be forever admired.

Read the passage. Answer the questions.

1 What is the best summary for the entire passage?
    a. With Annie's help, Helen went from being a wild, unruly child to an enthusiastic student.
    b. Helen Keller's childhood was difficult, but she went onto become a highly honored college graduate and traveled the world.
    c. An illness robbed Helen of her hearing and vision when she was a child.
    d. Annie Sullivan was a very persistent teacher.

2 What is the best title for the first paragraph?
    a. Helen's Life Story
    b. A Spoiled and Lonely Child
    c. A Horrible Child
    d. Annie Arrives

3 A good title for the last paragraph would be

_____.

Name _____ Date _____

Movie Buff

SUMMARIZING

Read each movie summary. Answer the questions.

Professional Dreamer Mike becomes a star basketball player, but only when he's sleep-walking. This comedy follows Mike through the championship game and helps him to see that he has more than just dreams of a basketball career.	**Polar Ice Cap** This documentary follows two explorers through a year-long expedition to the polar ice cap. Beautiful images and amazing facts about the history of this region will keep you interested for hours.
It Does Come Back This thriller will keep you on the edge of your seat. Three friends explore a scary house, only to discover visitors from another planet. And they are *not* friendly.	**Wild, Wild West** This historical drama tells the story of one family's journey West. The focus of this tale is the family's struggle with the harsh climate and rugged trail. The beauty of the Old West is almost another character in this moving and heart-filled story.

1 If you love a good scare, you would go see _____.

2 People who like nature would go see _____.

3 If you want a good laugh, you would go see _____.

4 History lovers will want to see _____.

5 Which movie is probably *not* appropriate for young children? _____

6 Which movie would you most like to see? _____

Reading Skills • 7–8 © 2004 Creative Teaching Press

Sum It Up

SUMMARIZING

Read each paragraph. Identify the topic. Then write a short summary of the paragraph.

1 Growing your own vegetable garden has many benefits. You will have access to the freshest vegetables. Never again will you need to stand in line to pick up a bruised and tasteless tomato from your local grocery store. You will also have total control over the use of chemicals on your produce. If you choose, you can have completely organic vegetables with only water to help them grow. There are other health benefits to gardening as well. You will get exercise while you tend the garden.

What is the topic? _____

Summary:

_____

_____

_____

2 Reading is a hobby for everyone. It helps you to expand your mind, and it is an inexpensive way to entertain yourself while experiencing worlds both near and far. Reading offers something for everyone because you can find books, newspapers, or magazines on any topic that interests you. Books can make you laugh, make you cry, scare you, educate you, and even help you to learn more about yourself. When you read, you bring your own life experiences to the story so that it becomes uniquely your own. No two people will interpret text in exactly the same way. Reading gives you the freedom to go anywhere, be anyone, and do anything.

What is the topic? _____

Summary:

_____

_____

_____

Short Summaries

SUMMARIZING

Read each paragraph. Identify the topic. Then write a short summary.

1 Fables are short, entertaining stories that cleverly depict animals with very human qualities. The animals speak, display emotion, and display traits such as vanity, pride, and ambition. Despite their entertainment value, the primary purpose of fables is to teach a lesson, or moral, by poking fun at our follies and selfish tendencies in an exaggerated way. Parents often read fables to young children to teach them to be virtuous, but young and old alike can enjoy and learn from fables.

What is the topic? _____

Summary:

_____

_____

_____

2 Pollution is something that should worry us all. We have only a limited amount of natural resources. Pollution significantly damages many of these, like our water and air. Cars and trucks send chemicals that pollute the air. Products like hair spray, spray paint, and even chemicals from our refrigerators and air conditioners can damage our environment. We must make an effort to be more responsible. We need to educate about these dangers and help others learn more, too. Our future depends on it.

What is the topic? _____

Summary:

_____

_____

_____

Name _____ Date _____

  # First or Third

POINT OF VIEW

> **Point of view** is the angle from which a story is told. Point of view varies depending on who tells the story. In **first person** point of view, one of the characters is telling the story. In **third person** point of view, someone outside is telling the story.
>
> **Example:**
> **first person**   *I told my mom that I wanted to walk home from school.*
> **third person**   *Amanda told her mom that she wanted to walk home from school.*

Read each sentence. Write **F** if it is written in first person point of view. Write **T** if it is written in third person point of view.

1 _____ She bought a newspaper on her way to work.

2 _____ The children followed the fire truck in the parade.

3 _____ I don't think we should waste time arguing.

4 _____ We celebrated the holiday at my aunt and uncle's cabin.

5 _____ Her cat jumped on the table and broke my glasses.

6 _____ She said, "I don't know what I'm going to do."

7 _____ The boy broke his arm when he fell from the tree.

8 _____ Why did you take my favorite notebook?

9 _____ "Did you make plans for vacation?" he asked.

10 _____ Our soccer team won a trophy for first place.

11 _____ We travel to Chicago, Illinois, to visit Aunt Becky every summer.

12 _____ He knew he could not go with me to the game on Saturday night.

13 _____ The star basketball player made the winning shot just as the buzzer sounded.

14 _____ I studied so hard for the test I knew I would do well.

Reading Skills • 7–8 © 2004 Creative Teaching Press

First to Third; Third to First

POINT OF VIEW

Rewrite each sentence. If it is written in the first person, rewrite it in third person. If the sentence is written in the third person, rewrite it in first person.

1 She left her book on the bus.

_____

2 They play soccer after school.

_____

3 I typed my paper on the computer in my mom's office.

_____

4 My uncle gave me a skateboard for my birthday.

_____

5 What color are her eyes?

_____

6 She took the shortcut home from her lesson.

_____

7 Do I need to have my dad sign this permission slip?

_____

8 Our basketball coach said we had real potential.

_____

9 The dog chased me around the block and up my driveway.

_____

10 His grandmother lives three hours from his house.

_____

Reading Skills • 7–8 © 2004 Creative Teaching Press

Fairy Tale Views

POINT OF VIEW

Fairy tale characters made the following statements. Match each first person account to the corresponding story. Write the letter of the story on the line. Some titles will be used more than once.

a. Cinderella
b. Jack and the Beanstalk
c. Little Red Riding Hood
d. Snow White

e. The Princess and the Pea
f. The Emperor's New Suit
g. The Little Red Hen
h. Hansel and Gretel

1 _____ I told her I don't make bread!

2 _____ I was amazed that he believed we were tailors!

3 _____ My brother took a bite off her door.

4 _____ My granddaughter should be coming any minute.

5 _____ My stepsister does all the work around the house.

6 _____ My mother has this thing about testing my girlfriends.

7 _____ I'm stuck traveling the kingdom and trying shoes on girls!

8 _____ My son is not very responsible. I can't even trust him to sell a cow.

9 _____ I whipped up this poison apple for her.

10 _____ I'm feeling a little chilly, but I look fabulous!

11 _____ You would think this palace would have more comfortable beds.

12 _____ The girl I was dancing with just ran off and left me!

Name _____ Date _____

Pick a Point

POINT OF VIEW

Read each scenario. Circle the choice that identifies the point of view.

1   "I'm not getting out of bed," I yelled.
There is no way I am climbing on that bus today. I rolled over and saw my reflection in the mirror on my door. I'm pretty sure the sun flashed off all the new metal that now covered my teeth.

　　　first person point of view　　　　　third person point of view

2   My class was chosen to represent the school in a statewide geography bee. We have been preparing for weeks. Mrs. Green, our teacher, created a game to help us learn new information and review what we already know. Mrs. Green says that she thinks we will do very well in the competition.

　　　first person point of view　　　　　third person point of view

3   The bus driver asked the team to quiet down. The rain was falling hard, and it was becoming very difficult to see the road.
"Do you think we should pull over?" asked Mr. Farrow, the coach.
"I think we'll be fine. I'll just try to make the next exit and then we'll stop for a dinner break," said the driver.

　　　first person point of view　　　　　third person point of view

4   Mrs. Pyka, our social studies teacher, assigned a report due next Wednesday. We get to choose our topic and a classmate to work with. Sarah and I will write about Clara Barton, founder of the American Red Cross.

　　　first person point of view　　　　　third person point of view

Reading Skills • 7–8 © 2004 Creative Teaching Press

Name _____ Date _____

What Do They Want?

DRAWING CONCLUSIONS

Read each scenario. Draw conclusions about what you think the character most wants. Answer the questions.

1 Kevin's mother is angry. She is tired of doing all the housecleaning alone. Kevin leaves his dirty clothes all over his bedroom floor. He also forgets to put away his toys and games. His mother has had enough.
What do you think Kevin's mother wants?
    a. a maid
    b. a vacation
    c. help from Kevin
    d. a bigger house

2 Sarah and Robert have just moved into a new house. They are still waiting for the movers to deliver their furniture. They are tired of eating and sleeping on the floor. Sarah also misses her favorite chair.
What do Sarah and Robert want?
    a. to move back to their old house
    b. to receive their things
    c. to make new friends
    d. to buy new furniture

3 Paul has been to every varsity basketball game. He will be eligible to try out next year. He wants to be sure that he knows all the plays that Coach Anderson runs. He takes notes and studies them carefully. He also makes sure to stay in top shape so he will be ready to make fast breaks.
What does Paul want?
    a. to make the varsity basketball team
    b. to help the coach at practice
    c. to help coach the varsity team
    d. to run a marathon

4 Isaac has been unusually helpful at home this week. Without being asked, he helped his little sister with her homework, he did two loads of laundry, and he kept his room spotless. Today he will tell his mother about the concert his friends are going to Saturday night.
What does Isaac want?
    a. to do more housework
    b. to go to the concert
    c. to stay home Saturday night
    c. to go to the ball game

What's Happening?

DRAWING CONCLUSIONS

Read each scenario. Draw conclusions about the event being described. Answer the questions.

1 Carmela and her sister went to their favorite restaurant for dinner Saturday night. Carmela ordered baked chicken, and her sister ordered fish, but they both had the garlic mashed potatoes. They enjoyed their meal, but within several hours, Carmela became very ill. Why?

_____

2 Brett had a great after-school job as a clerk at the local video store, but he never made it to work on time. He always stopped to enjoy a quick soda with his buddies, making him 10 minutes late. Brett liked having paychecks to spend on entertainment, and he was saving money for the college he wanted to attend. He also liked his boss, who told Brett that if he was late one more time, he was fired. What did Brett do?

_____

3 Trying to ignore the butterflies in her stomach, Lisa stretched her legs and glanced around at the other girls, who were doing the same. She decided not to think of them. She just looked beyond the ten white structures aligned perfectly in front of her to the line strung across the lanes. She and seven others took their mark and anticipated the "pop" of the pistol. What was Lisa doing?

_____

4 Benjamin held his ticket in his hand in front of the television set, watching the spinning machine spit out one numbered ball at a time. He stared in disbelief at the numbers he saw, his hands starting to shake, his face turning red. Benjamin kept looking from his ticket to the television and back again. He was in such a state of shock that he could not even speak. What had just happened?

_____

5 Carlos and Tina waited in the long line for over an hour, listening to the screams of the people who had gone before them. Finally, they were ushered onto the first seat of the car and strapped in. Tina's heart skipped a beat as the car started to roll, climbing a very steep incline. What were they doing?

_____

Reading Skills • 7–8 © 2004 Creative Teaching Press

What's the Word?

DRAWING CONCLUSIONS

Read each scenario. Draw conclusions to help you determine the meaning of the underlined word. Write your definition on the line.

1 "Thank you for removing the awful thorn from my sore paw," said the Lion to Androcles. "I hope I can <u>reciprocate</u> the favor some day."

_____

2 When a feeling of <u>nostalgia</u> comes over my mother, she plays music from the sixties and tells me stories about people she doesn't get to see very much anymore.

_____

3 St. George promised the princess that he would not <u>succumb</u> to the dragon's might. Indeed, he won the fierce battle and saved her people from certain death.

_____

4 The talking cat was just a <u>figment</u> of the young girl's imagination.

_____

5 The child received a small <u>terrarium</u> for her birthday. "Great!" she exclaimed. "Now my turtle has a real home instead of this old cardboard box. I bet he comes out of his shell a lot more often."

_____

6 The two friends had a bitter argument over the rules of chess. After two weeks of not speaking to one another, they <u>reconciled</u>, realizing that it was childish to fight about something so petty.

_____

7 Escorted by a police officer, a somber man walked into the courtroom, his gaze fixed upon the <u>manacles</u> around his ankles. They clanged with every step, reminding the prisoner that his freedom may be lost.

_____

8 The <u>benevolence</u> of the mysterious stranger brought the homeless man to tears. Not only did he bring the hungry man food, he gave the man money for a hotel room on the extremely cold night.

_____

Experimental Conclusions

DRAWING CONCLUSIONS

Read each science experiment. Describe the conclusion you can make about the experiment.

Experiment 1

Using a balance scale, you place a cup of marbles on one end. On the other side, you place a rock found on the playground. The scale immediately tips so that the cup is in the air and the side with the rock is touching the table.

What conclusion can you make?

_____

_____

_____

Experiment 2

You take your resting pulse and find out that it is 75 beats per minute. Then you jump rope for one minute and take your pulse again. This time it is 140 beats per minute. After a rest period, you walk up the stairs and take your pulse for a third time. This time it is 100 beats per minute.

What conclusion can you make?

_____

_____

_____

Experiment 3

You fill two glasses with water. Then you add a tablespoon of vinegar to one of the glasses. Next you place a tablespoon of baking soda in both glasses. The solution with the vinegar and baking soda immediately begins to bubble. The glass with only water does nothing.

What conclusion can you make?

_____

_____

_____

Experiment 4

You cover five leaves on a plant with aluminum foil. Then you place the plant in a sunny window and water it regularly. After one week, you remove the foil from the leaves. You notice that the leaves that were not covered are green and strong. The leaves that were covered have turned yellow and feel limp.

What conclusion can you make?

_____

_____

_____

Reading Skills • 7–8 © 2004 Creative Teaching Press

It's All in the Title

Main Idea and Supporting Details

Read each paragraph. Circle the letter of the best title for the paragraph.

1 If you are researching a topic, the best way to find information is to use a search engine on the Internet. First, ask a librarian or teacher to help you locate the best search engine for your research. Next, determine a keyword or two. The keyword is a word or phrase that relates to your topic. Type in your keyword and click on "Search." You may need to experiment with different keywords to find the one that is most useful. The search engine will suggest a number of resources for you to review. Browse through the suggestions and choose the ones that are most helpful. Remember to always double-check the accurateness of the sources you use.

  a. Choosing a Keyword
  b. How to Use a Search Engine
  c. Research and Keywords
  d. The Internet Is Not Always Accurate

2 The invention of farm machinery greatly increased agricultural production and decreased the need for manual labor. Before the use of farm machines, it took about 40–50 labor hours and 5 acres of land to produce 100 bushels of wheat on one farm. The invention of machines like the steel plow, farm wagon, thresher, and other equipment made it possible to produce the same amount of wheat in only three hours on 3 acres of land. Such machinery changed the world of farming forever.

  a. More Manual Labor
  b. Wheat Production
  c. The Effects of Farm Machinery
  d. Kinds of Farm Equipment

3 Making your own globe is a fun and easy way to learn more about geography. Begin by inflating a large, round balloon. Then cover the balloon with at least four layers of papier-mâché (newspaper strips dipped into a flour-and-water mixture). Let the strips dry overnight. Then, using an actual globe as a reference, add the continents with green paint and the oceans with blue paint. Finally, use a black felt-tip marker to add details and label specific features.

  a. Making Papier-Mâché
  b. Balloons are More Than Fun
  c. Learning about Geography
  d. Making Your Own Globe

Name the Article

Main Ideas and Supporting Details

Read each story from a school newspaper. Identify the main idea. Write the matching title above the article.

One Student's Triumph
Future Plans Announced

Lunch Room Rules
History Brought to Life

_____

1 A local theater group visited Greenburg School on Friday to present a play called *The Way It Was*. The play is a collection of stories about the founding of our town. Local historians interviewed 25 citizens to gather information and memories about events that brought our town together. The play was a real lesson from the past.

_____

2 Megan Rider returned to school today after recovering from a terrible biking accident. Megan broke her leg and arm in the collision that left her unconscious for a brief time. After six weeks of difficult rehab, Megan is walking without the assistance of her crutches. She wants to thank everyone who sent cards and letters while she was away.

_____

3 Students are no longer permitted to bring soda into the cafeteria. School officials are hoping to promote a healthier diet by making this restriction. Students will be allowed to bring milk, juice, and bottled water.

_____

4 The building committee unveiled the drawings for the new gymnasium yesterday. The new building will be twice the size of the current one. A new scoreboard and locker rooms will also be added. The sports program will greatly benefit from these changes.

Reading Skills • 7–8 © 2004 Creative Teaching Press

Main Idea

MAIN IDEA AND SUPPORTING DETAILS

Read each paragraph. Choose the sentence that best summarizes the main idea.

1 The journey took six days. We started out early each day and hiked until lunch. We were careful to take many breaks. It was really important to drink a lot of water. As we began to reach the higher elevations, we learned to slow our steps down a bit. The air was much thinner and it became difficult to get a deep breath. The hard work was more than worth it when we reached the top of the mountain. The view was amazing.
Which sentence best summarizes the main idea?
   a. Camping outside made our hike difficult.
   b. We needed to carry a lot of water for our hike.
   c. Climbing the mountain was difficult but rewarding.
   d. Mountain climbing requires special equipment.

2 Watercolors tend to bleed more, which makes them difficult to control. Acrylic paint is thicker and tends not to run. Acrylics also give more options for creating raised textures on the canvas. Watercolors are often used to create a subtle, almost dreamlike quality to a painting. Many artists like to experiment with both paint types to find the one they prefer.
Which sentence best summarizes the main idea?
   a. Watercolors are better than acrylic paints.
   b. Artists must choose between acrylics and watercolor paints.
   c. Both watercolors and acrylic paints can be used.
   d. Watercolors and acrylic paints offer different options for painters.

3 We met early on Saturday. Everyone wore work clothes and brought gloves. We formed two teams. One group pulled weeds and prepared the flowerbeds. The second group planted flowers at the school's entrance. After several hours of work, we could see a real difference.
Which sentence best summarizes the main idea?
   a. Our class decided to improve the look of our school.
   b. Volunteers are difficult to find at our school.
   c. Some people think we should plant trees and flowers.
   d. Planting flowers is work best done by adults.

Statement Identification

MAIN IDEA AND SUPPORTING DETAILS

Remember that a **main idea statement** catches the reader's attention and gives the focus of the paragraph. A **supporting detail** tells more information about the topic or experience.

Read each set of sentences. Write **M** to identify the main idea statement. Write **S** to identify each detail.

1 _____ They are made into food products for people all over the world.
_____ Wheat, corn, and soybeans are major crops for Middle America.
_____ Straw for baskets and even some plastics can be made from wheat.
_____ Parts of these plants are made into other products as well.
_____ Soy can be used to make medicine.

2 _____ The car began to sputter and stall.
_____ We were only on the highway for a short time when it began.
_____ We needed to walk for a mile to find a gas station.
_____ Our trip to the beach did not go the way we planned.
_____ My dad got a funny look on his face when he noticed the gas gauge.

3 _____ First, scientists learned to change light and sound into electronic signals.
_____ Soon they could turn these signals back into sounds and light in your TV.
_____ Scientific discoveries in the late 1800s led to the invention of the television.
_____ Then they discovered how to send these signals.
_____ Each of these devices paved the way to the creation of television.

4 _____ Creating a fire safety plan is easy and important for your family's safety.
_____ Choose a safe meeting place outside your house.
_____ Discuss various escape routes from our house.
_____ Practice by conducting a fire drill at least once each month.
_____ Make sure that everyone knows to call 9-1-1 from a safe location.

5 _____ At the age of twelve, my brother has mastered the guitar.
_____ A radio tuned to a classical music station plays continually in the baby's room.
_____ Mom and Dad take us to listen to live music of all kinds.
_____ My parents think it's important to learn music appreciation very early in life.
_____ I was enrolled in piano lessons when I was five years old.

Reading Skills • 7–8 © 2004 Creative Teaching Press

Name _____ Date _____

Which One Doesn't Belong?

Main Idea and Supporting Details

Read each main idea statement. Draw an X next to the detail that does not support the main idea.

1 Proper cleanup of your campsite is important.
_____ You must be sure that your campfire has been completely extinguished.
_____ Never leave food lying around because it will attract wild animals.
_____ Camping trailers are a good way to enjoy the outdoors.
_____ Be sure to pick up all garbage and dispose of it properly.

2 Al and Tom are looking forward to their visit to the museum.
_____ They have been planning the trip for weeks.
_____ The museum has an exhibit on Egypt.
_____ Both boys bought museum guidebooks to learn about the exhibits.
_____ Al saved his allowance to buy a special souvenir.

3 Learning about the constellations is a fun summer hobby.
_____ You can spend hours searching for star patterns in the night sky.
_____ Looking up the history of the constellations will keep you very busy.
_____ It is much more pleasant to star gaze in warmer weather.
_____ The North Star was often used by sailors to navigate their ships.

4 Many factors led to the American Civil War.
_____ The North and South disagreed over slavery.
_____ The Northern people were often called "Yankees."
_____ Both sides disagreed over how new states should enter the Union.
_____ People in the North had very different political views than those in the South.

5 Computers have changed the way we live, learn, and work.
_____ E-mail makes it possible for many people to work from home.
_____ Students can use the Internet to do research and get homework help.
_____ Some people even do their grocery shopping from their home computer.
_____ Keyboarding lessons are helpful when you want to type quickly.

6 Listening is an important skill for doctors to have.
_____ Doctors see many different patients in the course of a day.
_____ Listening to a patient's symptoms can help a doctor to make a correct diagnosis.
_____ Patients feel more comfortable with a doctor who takes the time to listen.
_____ Unnecessary tests can be avoided if doctors pay attention to what patients say.

Reading Skills • 7-8 © 2004 Creative Teaching Press

Name _____ Date _____

Volunteer Persuasion

MAIN IDEA AND SUPPORTING DETAILS

All students should volunteer in their local community. Volunteering is a great way to learn responsibility. Students gain a sense of pride and ownership over the place in which they live while helping others. Studies show that many students who devote just one hour each week to community involvement score higher on standardized tests. These students are also less likely to get into trouble.

Communities also benefit from students who volunteer. One small town was able to develop three new parks through the efforts of student volunteers. Some groups have even partnered students with senior citizens to provide assistance or just companionship. There are numerous ways students can become involved in positive volunteering opportunities. The benefits are worth the effort.

Read the persuasive argument. Answer the questions.

1 What is the main idea of this passage?
   a. Senior citizens need help.
   b. Students are good at creating parks.
   c. Towns should pay students for their work.
   d. All students should volunteer.

2 Which statement does **not** support the main idea?
   a. Students learn responsibility by volunteering.
   b. Students who volunteer are less likely to get into trouble.
   c. Many students don't have time to volunteer.
   d. Many students who volunteer score higher on standardized tests.

3 What is a second main point of this passage?
   a. Not all students choose to volunteer.
   b. Communities also benefit from student volunteering.
   c. One hour a week is enough volunteer time.
   d. Some senior citizens need companionship.

4 The author of this passage would mostly agree with which statement?
   a. Adults should also volunteer.
   b. People should only volunteer when they are young.
   c. Only people in small towns should volunteer
   d. Students who volunteer are likely to litter.

Reading Skills • 7–8 © 2004 Creative Teaching Press

What Happened Next?

PREDICTING OUTCOMES

Read each sentence starter and predict the most logical outcome. Write the letter of the best ending on the line.

1. ____ I forgot to set the timer on the oven
2. ____ Adam studied hard
3. ____ The child fell off her bike
4. ____ We forgot to bring our money
5. ____ The printer was out of ink
6. ____ He forgot to plug in the toaster
7. ____ I didn't set my alarm clock
8. ____ My pencil broke
9. ____ The stamp fell off my letter
10. ____ The gas tank read "E" and
11. ____ Mom didn't turn on the clothes dryer
12. ____ I lost my umbrella
13. ____ We let go of our helium balloons
14. ____ I went to bed early last night
15. ____ She didn't eat breakfast
16. ____ He returned the lost wallet
17. ____ We misplaced the grocery list
18. ____ The girl followed the recipe exactly
19. ____ I planned every detail of the trip
20. ____ The electricity went off

a. so I couldn't write the answers.

b. then the car stalled.

c. so everything went smoothly.

d. so I overslept.

e. and we couldn't see in the dark.

f. and the cake turned out perfectly.

g. so we couldn't buy a souvenir.

h. and did well on his test.

i. so the bread burned.

j. and she was hungry all morning.

k. and saw them soar into the sky.

l. and was rewarded for his honesty.

m. so the bread never popped up.

n. so the post office returned it.

o. so I couldn't print.

p. and I feel very rested.

q. and she cried for her mother.

r. so I got wet in the rain.

s. so we didn't know what to buy.

t. so our laundry was still wet.

Reading Skills • 7–8 © 2004 Creative Teaching Press

And Then . . .

PREDICTING OUTCOMES

Read each scenario. Circle the letter of the event that will most likely happen next.

1 Marta's brother borrowed her radio without asking. He used it and forgot to turn it off when he was finished. When Marta went to use the radio, she couldn't find it. After searching through the house, she found it in her brother's room. The batteries no longer worked.

    a. Marta will reward her brother.
    b. Marta will be angry with her brother.
    c. Marta will be angry with her mother.
    d. Marta's brother will buy her a new radio.

2 A contest is being held to design a new logo for a local sports team. Jim is a great artist and a fan of the team. His mother brought home information regarding the contest and left it with Jim to read.

    a. Jim will throw the information away.
    b. Jim will be upset when he reads the information.
    c. Jim will want to enter the contest.
    d. Jim will look for a new team to support.

3 Mr. Bronsen, the custodian, found some graffiti written on a school locker. He shared the information with the principal who called an assembly of all the students.

    a. The principal will review the school rules on vandalism.
    b. The principal will reward the custodian.
    c. The custodian will reward the students.
    d. The teachers will put on a show.

4 Donna cleaned the house and made dinner before her mother came home from work. She also finished her homework and helped her brother with his. Her mother arrived home to the smell of her favorite meal.

    a. Donna will be in trouble.
    b. Donna will expect a reward for her work.
    c. Donna will tell her mother that her brother did the work.
    d. Donna's mother will thank her for her hard work.

Reading Skills • 7–8 © 2004 Creative Teaching Press

What Is That About?

PREDICTING OUTCOMES

Read each book title. Circle the letter of the description that tells what the book is most likely about.

1 *The Trouble with Scooters*
a. a history of scooters
b. problems associated with scooters
c. the story of people who ride scooters
d. a book about snails

2 *My Rise to Stardom*
a. an astronaut's autobiography
b. the autobiography of a president
c. the story of starfish
d. a celebrity's autobiography

3 *The Best Way to Make Friends*
a. the story of a person's friends
b. a self-help book on making friends
c. a cookbook for large groups
d. a book on hypnosis

4 *Places to Visit in Canada*
a. a cookbook of Canadian food
b. a travel guide of Hawaii
c. a travel guide of Canada
d. a book of poetry

5 *Knock, Knock: Who's There?*
a. the story of doors
b. a book of knock, knock jokes
c. a science book about sound
d. a music book about percussion

6 *A Guide to Homemade Dinners*
a. a book of dinner recipes
b. a book with pictures of people's dinners
c. a travel guide
d. the biography of a chef

7 *Mickey Mouse: The Untold Story*
a. a travel guide for Florida
b. a biography of Mickey Mouse
c. an amusement part guide
d. a book of photography

8 *Photography of the Northeast*
a. a book on how to take pictures
b. the biography of a photographer
c. pictures of places in the Northeast
d. a history of photography

9 *Verses for Spring*
a. a cookbook for fresh vegetables
b. a nature guide
c. the science of spring
d. a book of spring poetry

10 *Songs to Play When You're Sad*
a. a cookbook for one
b. a manual for car radios
c. a songbook for musicians
d. a biography of a musician

Name _____ Date _____

More Predictions

PREDICTING OUTCOMES

Read each scenario. Circle the letter of the most logical outcome for each situation.

1 Abraham, nicknamed Honest Abe by his classmates, accidentally backs into the trashcans in his mother's car and badly scratches its bumper and dents the cans.
   a. He will pretend nothing happened and wait for her to ask him what happened.
   b. He will paint over the scratch.
   c. He will be grounded for two weeks.
   d. He will tell his mother and apologize before she sees it.

2 Sam rides his bike home from school. Without knowing it, his tire hits a nail. Sam parks his bike in the garage and goes in for the night.
   a. Sam will ride his bike to school again the next day.
   b. Sam will find the tire has fallen off his bike.
   c. Sam will find his brakes no longer work.
   d. Sam will find a flat tire the next morning.

3 Jessica received a plant from her grandmother. She put it on her dresser and forgot about it. She remembered it three weeks later.
   a. Jessica's plant will probably be dead.
   b. Jessica's plant will not look any different.
   c. The plant will be gone from her room.
   d. Jessica will only find dirt in the pot.

4 Emma works very hard on every project she undertakes, whether it's sewing a skirt or planning a party. She is known as a true perfectionist, successful at everything she does. Emma and two friends are starting a new business of making and selling one-of-a-kind handbags.
   a. Emma will be too busy to make much time for the new business.
   b. Emma will let her friends take care of the details.
   c. Emma will make the new business a priority and work hard at it.
   d. Emma will be bossy and unpleasant to work with.

Reading Skills • 7–8 © 2004 Creative Teaching Press

Who and Where?

STORY ELEMENTS

Lisa knew the first day of high school wouldn't be easy. She was starting her fifth school in seven years. Her father's job required her family to move often. The first day in a new place was always the hardest.

Stepping off the bus, Lisa dropped her bag. Her notebook and pencils went flying. Scrambling to pick them up, several students passed her, laughing and whispering. Just when Lisa thought she couldn't get more flustered, a blond boy with a friendly smile knelt down to help her gather her belongings.

"Hi, I'm Andrew," he said as they both stood up. "Are you new?"

"Um, yeah. My name is Lisa," she replied shyly.

"Welcome to McWayne Middle School. I hope the rest of your day goes better than your exit from the bus," said Andrew handing Lisa the last of her pens.

"Me, too. Thanks," said Lisa. As she turned to walk away, her lunch slipped out of her bag and fell on the sidewalk.

"Hey, wait up. Why don't you let me show you around? Looks like you could use a friend," called Andrew.

"Sure, that would be great," said Lisa, bending to pick up her lunch bag.

She looked up at the doors of McWayne Middle School and smiled for the first time that day.

Read the story. Answer the questions about character and setting.

1 Where does this story take place?
    a. in the cafeteria
    b. outside the school
    c. at Lisa's house
    d. in the bus

2 At the beginning, how do you know that Lisa is **not** excited about her new school?
    a. she says the first day is always the hardest
    b. she refuses to go
    c. she cries
    d. she drops her bag

3 Which word best describes Lisa?
    a. resilient
    b. timid
    c. snobby
    d. graceful

4 Which of the following best describes Andrew?
    a. ill-mannered
    b. uninterested
    c. considerate
    d. confused

5 How do you think the rest of Lisa's day will go? Use examples from the story to support your answer.

_____

_____

Dialogue Drawings
STORY ELEMENTS

Look carefully at each drawing. Write at least two lines of dialogue for each picture. Be creative and use the pictures clues.

1 _____

_____

_____

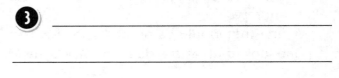

3 _____

_____

_____

2 _____

_____

_____

4 _____

_____

_____

Reading Skills • 7–8 © 2004 Creative Teaching Press

Name _____ Date _____

It's All About the Moral

STORY ELEMENTS

Read each story. Circle the letter of the statement that best describes the moral of each story.

1 A black crow had stolen a large piece of meat. Pleased with her meal, she flew to a branch in the woods, holding the meat in her beak. A clever fox came along and envied that piece of meat. He told the crow what a beautiful bird she was with her feathers so fine! He asked her if her song was as beautiful. Flattered by his words, she opened her mouth to sing for him and down fell the prized meat. The fox caught it in his jaws and happily ran away.

    a. Crows are not as clever as foxes.
    b. Villagers cannot be trusted to help children in need.
    c. Too much pride will not serve us well.
    d. Foxes will always come back.

2 A peacock spread its gorgeous tail and mocked a crane that passed by him. He remarked on the crane's drab colors, and bragged that his own kingly colors were more beautiful than a rainbow. The crane replied that though his colors were not bright, he could fly to great heights and lift his voice to the stars, while the peacock was left to walk below with bugs and snakes.

    a. Peacocks are mean birds.
    b. Colorful birds have no real value.
    c. A bird that can fly will be colorless and drab.
    d. Fine feathers don't make fine birds.

Reading Skills • 7–8 © 2004 Creative Teaching Press

Plot Line

STORY ELEMENTS

The **plot** is the action or series of events that make up the story. The plot line helps you keep track of the events in the story. Most stories, novels, and other works of fiction have a plot line with the following five parts:
1. exposition = introduction
2. rising action = suspense, tells the problems faced by the characters
3. climax = final battle, the highest point of suspense
4. falling action = what happens after the climax
5. resolution = the ending, or aftermath

Number each set of steps according to the order in which they would occur in the plot line.

1 _____ Lee notices his grandfather walking toward him with the dog.

_____ Lee and his dog visit his grandparents' house on weekends.

_____ After coming home from a walk, Lee notices the front gate open.

_____ Grandpa had taken the dog for a walk and forgotten to shut the gate.

_____ He searches frantically for some sign of his dog.

2 _____ The judges award them the prize without ever knowing about the accident.

_____ As they are walking to the judges' table, Jake trips.

_____ Jake and Mia enter a baking contest.

_____ Just before the dish hits the floor, Mia manages to catch it.

_____ On the day of the competition, they work hard to finish their dish on time.

3 _____ Al and Sue choose a beautiful necklace to buy for Mom's birthday present.

_____ Al reminds her that she gave him the money to hold.

_____ Sue opens her wallet and finds it empty.

_____ Just as she begins to panic, Al opens his wallet and takes out the money.

_____ She checks her purse, but there is nothing there either.

Reading Skills • 7–8 © 2004 Creative Teaching Press

Reading a Table of Contents

USING TEXT ORGANIZERS

Use the table of contents to answer the questions.

Table of Contents
Introduction **1**
I. Basics **5**
    1. Fractions 7
    2. Equivalents 12
    3. Averages 20
    4. Multiples 30
II. Measurement **36**
    5. Centimeters 38
    6. Millimeters 45
    7. Perimeter 49
    8. Diameter 56
    9. Area 63
    10. Mass 69
    11. Weight 75
III. Graphing **82**
    12. Bar Graph 84
    13. Line Graph 88
    14. Pictograph 95
    15. Circle Graph 99
Glossary **108**
Index **118**

1 What is the subject of this book? _____

2 How many chapters are in this book? _____

3 What page is the *first* page of Chapter 10? _____

4 What is the *last* page of Chapter 7? _____

5 What would you learn about in Section III? _____

6 Which chapter would tell you how to interpret a bar graph? _____

7 Which chapter would tell you how to find perimeter? _____

8 What page would you turn to if you wanted to learn about circle graphs? _____

9 How many chapters are in the **Measurement** section? _____

10 How many pages are in the glossary? _____

Using a Glossary

USING TEXT ORGANIZERS

Use the glossary to answer the questions.

A

acceleration the rate of change of velocity

axon part of the nerve cell that carries impulses away from the cell body

B

bacteria group of microscopic, one-celled organisms

bile a bitter greenish-yellow liquid released by the liver that aids in digestion

C

cell the basic living unit of an organism

circuit a closed path through which current flows

D

digestion the breaking down of food into forms animals can use

E

electron negatively charged particle that moves around the nucleus of an atom

F

force a push or a pull.

fulcrum point on which a lever is supported and turns

G

gene a unit of information that controls a trait

---

1 Which word means "a push or a pull"? _____

2 What is a cell? _____

3 How many words in the glossary begin with A? _____

4 What is the definition of *fulcrum*? _____

5 How many total entries are in this glossary? _____

6 Which word means "the rate of change of velocity"? _____

7 What is the definition of *electron*? _____

8 Circle the correct definition of *gene*.
   a. a push or a pull
   b. group of microscopic, one-celled organisms
   c. the basic living unit of an organism
   d. a unit of information that controls a trait

Reading Skills • 7–8 © 2004 Creative Teaching Press

Using an Index

USING TEXT ORGANIZERS

Aardvarks, 27, 293
Africa, 19, 53, 103, 146
Allergy, 212, 292

Bison, 135, 269
Bronx Zoo, 24
Butterflies, 86, 284–286

Camels, 30, 45, 289
Caterpillar, 264, 297

Drought, 146–150
Dust, 114, 118, 239

Jaguars, 293
Jellyfish, 292

Opossums, 279
Oysters, 301

Raccoons, 36
Rhinoceros, 30, 316

Yak, 62, 79, 160
Yellow Jackets, 45–46

Zoo, 24, 35, 48–51, 167, 214, 278

List the page(s) where you could find information about each topic.

1 Aardvarks _____

2 The Bronx Zoo _____

3 Yellow Jackets _____

4 Jellyfish _____

5 Dust _____

6 Raccoons _____

7 Camels _____

8 Oysters _____

9 Africa _____

10 Bison _____

11 Drought _____

12 Which topic appears most often in this book? Which pages include this topic?

_____

Understanding a Bibliography
USING TEXT ORGANIZERS

Use the bibliography to answer the questions.

Bermingham, Ellen. *The Bill of Rights and You.* Cambridge, Mass.: Harvard Unity Press, 2004.

"Do You Know Your Rights?" *Time for Kids* (December 2001) 35–46.

Everhart, Richard. *Constitutional Freedoms.* San Francisco, CA: Chandler Press, 1999.

Hemrich, Dennis. "My Rights, Your Rights." *Atlantic* (February 2000) 29–34.

Tyler, Marsha. "The New Civil Rights Movement," *New York Times,* Sunday, 24 February 2001, sec. 4.

1 What is the name of the book written by Ellen Bermingham? _____

2 On what pages would you find the article "Do You Know Your Rights?" _____

3 Who wrote "My Rights, Your Rights"? _____

4 In what newspaper does Marsha Tyler's article appear? _____

5 What section of the newspaper would you find Marsha Tyler's article? _____

6 What year was Ellen Bermingham's book published? _____

7 Who published Richard Everhart's book? _____

8 What is the name of the magazine in which Dennis Hemrich's article appears?

_____

9 Which issue of *Time for Kids* was referenced in this bibliography? _____

10 Where is Chandler Press located? _____

Reading Skills • 7–8 © 2004 Creative Teaching Press

Name _____ Date _____

Interpreting a Bar Graph
INTERPRETING GRAPHIC ORGANIZERS

Use the bar graph to answer the questions.

How Fast Do Animals Run?

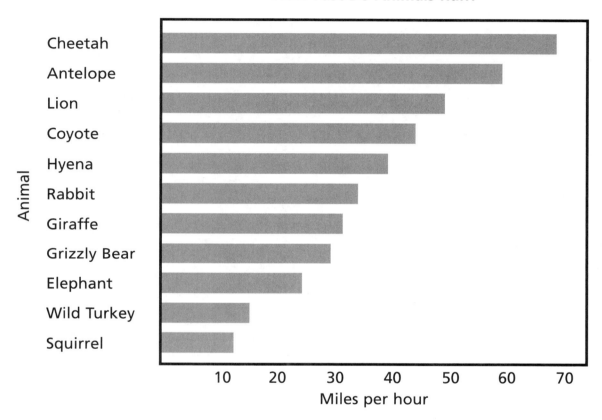

1 Which animal runs the fastest? _____

2 Which animal runs the slowest? _____

3 How fast does a hyena run? _____

4 Which is faster, a grizzly bear or a coyote? By how much? _____

5 How much faster is a lion than an elephant? _____

6 If a rabbit and a giraffe were in a race, which would win? _____

7 How much slower is a wild turkey than an antelope? _____

8 What is the difference between the fastest and slowest animals? _____

Reading Skills • 7–8 © 2004 Creative Teaching Press

Name _____ Date _____

Interpreting Charts

INTERPRETING GRAPHIC ORGANIZERS

Use the pie chart to answer the questions.

What makes up the air around the Earth?

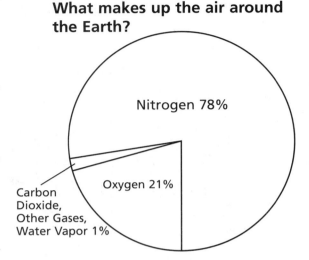

1 How much of the air is made up of oxygen?

_____

2 What gas makes up most of the Earth's air?

_____

3 How much of the air is composed of oxygen and nitrogen?

_____

4 How much of the air is **not** made up of nitrogen? _____

5 How much of the air is **not** made up of oxygen? _____

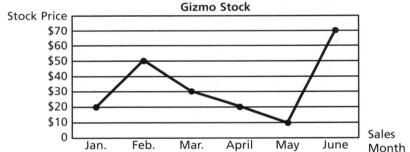

Use the stock chart to answer the questions.

6 In what month did Gizmo stock hit its lowest price? What was the price?

_____

7 How much did the price change from January to June? _____

8 How much was Gizmo stock selling for in March? _____

9 What was the price difference from March to May? _____

10 Was the price difference from February to May positive or negative? How much was the difference?

_____

Reading Skills • 7–8 © 2004 Creative Teaching Press

Name _____ Date _____

Interpreting a Table

INTERPRETING GRAPHIC ORGANIZERS

8 Largest Cities (as of 2000)	
City, Country	**Population**
Tokyo, Japan	26,440,000
Mexico City, Mexico	18,131,000
Bombay, India	18,066,000
São Paulo, Brazil	17,755,000
New York City, U.S.	16,640,000
Lagos, Nigeria	13,427,000
Los Angeles, U.S.	13,140,000
Calcutta, India	12,918,000

Use the table to answer the questions.

1 Which city has the largest population? How many people live there?

_____

2 How many people live in New York City? _____

3 In what country is Bombay?_____

4 Which cities in India made the top eight list?_____

5 How many countries have more than one city on the list?_____

6 What is the population of Lagos, Nigeria? _____

7 How many more people live in Tokyo than Calcutta? _____

8 How many fewer people live in Los Angeles than São Paulo?_____

9 How many people live in Lagos, Los Angeles, and Calcutta combined? _____

10 Which cities would make the list of "5 Largest Cities" as of 2000?

_____

Reading Skills • 7–8 © 2004 Creative Teaching Press

Interpreting a Timeline

INTERPRETING GRAPHIC ORGANIZERS

Use the timeline to answer the questions.

April 12, 1961
Soviet cosmonaut Yuri
Gagarin is first human
in space.

February 20, 1962
John Glenn is first
American to orbit
Earth.

June 16, 1963
Soviet Valentina
Tereshkova is first
woman in space.

March 18, 1965
Soviet Alexei Leonov
is first person to walk
in space.

July 20, 1969
America's Neil
Armstrong is first
person to walk on
the moon.

December 7, 1972
Final U.S. space mission
to land on the moon.

May 14, 1973
U.S. puts space station
into orbit.

July 15, 1975
Last U.S. space mission
of the Apollo era.

1 When did the first American enter space?

_____

2 Who was the first woman in space?

_____

3 Which country was the first to enter space?

_____

4 What was the date of the last U.S. space landing
on the moon?

_____

5 What happened in 1965?

_____

6 Who was the first person to walk on the moon?

_____

7 When did the first American walk on the moon?

_____

8 How long after the first space mission did the
U.S. enter space?

_____

9 When did the U.S. put a space station into orbit?

_____

10 Who was the first human in space?

_____

Reading Skills • 7–8 © 2004 Creative Teaching Press

Name _____ Date _____

Interpreting a Diagram
INTERPRETING GRAPHIC ORGANIZERS

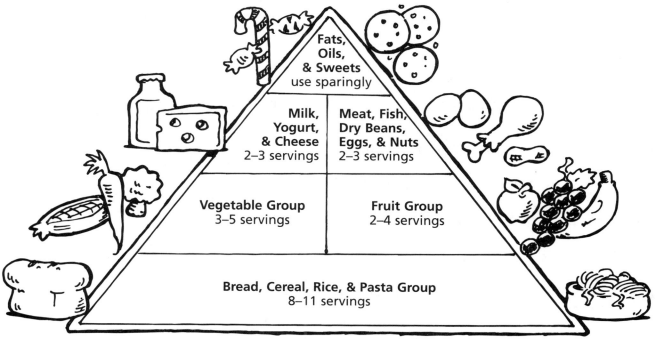

The Food Guide Pyramid suggests how many servings of different kinds of foods you should eat each day.

Use the food pyramid to answer the questions.

1 From which food group should you eat the most? _____

2 Which type of food should you eat the least? _____

3 How many servings of fruit should be in your daily diet? _____

4 Name three food items that would be in the vegetable category. _____

_____

5 Name two examples of foods you would find in the Fats, Oils, & Sweets category.

_____

6 What does "use sparingly" mean? _____

7 How many servings from the meat category should you eat in one day? _____

8 What does the food pyramid show? _____

Reading Skills • 7–8 © 2004 Creative Teaching Press

Using a Thesaurus

USING REFERENCE MATERIALS

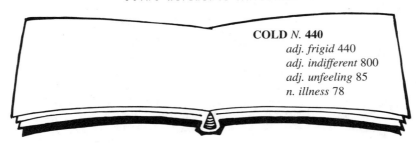

COLD *N.* **440**
adj. frigid 440
adj. indifferent 800
adj. unfeeling 85
n. illness 78

Use the thesaurus index to answer the questions.

1 How many guide words are listed for the word *cold*? _____

2 What do the abbreviations *adj.* and *n.* stand for? _____

3 Which guide word would give you a synonym for a cold temperature? _____

4 Which guide word would give you a synonym for the cold that makes you sneeze?

_____

440. COLD—*N.* **cold,** coldness
snow, snowflake, snowball
ice, sleet, hail, icicle, freezing rain
adj. **cold,** frigid, chilly, icy, freezing,
numbing, cool, frosty, frozen, frostbitten

frigid, refrigerated, bitter, biting, cutting,
nipping

441. HOT—*N.* heat, warmth
adj. **hot,** warm, boiling, burning, muggy

Use the thesaurus entry to answer the questions.

5 List two synonyms for the word *cold* that are adjectives. _____

6 What is the guide number for *cold*?_____

7 Name a synonym for the word *frigid*. _____

8 What is the guide number for the antonym for *cold*? _____

9 Use at least two different synonyms for the word *cold* in a sentence.

_____

_____

Reading Skills • 7–8 © 2004 Creative Teaching Press

Using a Dictionary

USING REFERENCE MATERIALS

Answer the following questions about using a dictionary.

1 Which set of guide words would you look between to find the word *sparrow*?
   a. speech/squeeze
   b. spadix/speak
   c. soak/spade
   d. sat/scour

2 What does the abbreviation *adv.* stand for?
   a. adverb
   b. adjective
   c. advance
   d. accent mark

3 Which of the following shows a pronunciation key?
   a. *interj.*
   b. [see picture]
   c. **school**
   d. [ˈskül]

4 The word *pho•to•graph* is divided to show
   a. parts of speech.
   b. syllable division.
   c. pronunciation.
   d. meaning.

[1]**spark** [ˈspärk] *n.* **1.** A bright particle, such as one let off from a fire or from friction. **2.** A short flash of light, such as from an electrical discharge.

[2]**spark** *v.* **1.** To set in motion. **2.** To inspire. *Her speech sparked a great deal of interest in our cause.*

Use the dictionary entry to answer the questions.

5 What is the entry word in this dictionary excerpt?
   a. speech
   b. bright
   c. spark
   d. set

6 Why is the word *spark* shown twice?
   a. The entries are homographs and are different parts of speech.
   b. They are spelled differently.
   c. The entries are pronounced differently.
   d. There is an error in the dictionary.

7 What is the purpose of the sentence at the end of the second entry?
   a. It helps to clarify the meaning.
   b. It helps with pronunciation.
   c. It has no purpose.
   d. It is a definition.

8 How many different definitions of the word *spark* are shown?
   a. 2
   b. 3
   c. 1
   d. 4

Name _____ Date _____

Using an Internet Search Engine

USING REFERENCE MATERIALS

> An **Internet search engine** is a useful tool for research. When using a search engine, it is important to choose **keywords**. Keywords are synonyms or phrases used to describe your topic.

Look at each topic. Draw a line through the keyword or phrase that would **not** be useful in your search.

1 Topic: The Egyptian Pyramids
pharaohs
pyramids
rainfall
ancient Egyptians

2 Topic: Dog Training
puppy schools
history of dogs
positive reinforcement for dogs
leash training

After running your search for "dog training," the search engine provided the following Web sites. Write the letter of the site or sites that best answers each question.

A. Dr. Wilson's Dog Training & Behavior Page
Noncommercial, comprehensive site on all aspects of dog training and behavior.

B. Dog Training Basics
Easy-to-follow steps to training your dog at home.

C. American Dog Trainers Association
Organization for professional dog trainers. Listing of current job openings. Password required.

D. Wholesale Dog Supplies—Training Supplies
Online catalog of all dog supplies, including training leashes.

---

3 _____ If you are writing a paper on dog training, which site or sites would be helpful?

4 _____ Where would you look to find the price of a training leash?

5 _____ If you wanted to learn to train your dog, which site or sites would you not use?

6 _____ If you were interested in a career in dog training, where would you look?

7 _____ Which site tells you that it is not selling anything?

8 _____ Which site or sites require a password?

Reading Skills • 7–8 © 2004 Creative Teaching Press

Using an Encyclopedia

USING REFERENCE MATERIALS

Look at the encyclopedia set. Determine which volume would contain information about each topic. Write the volume number on the line.

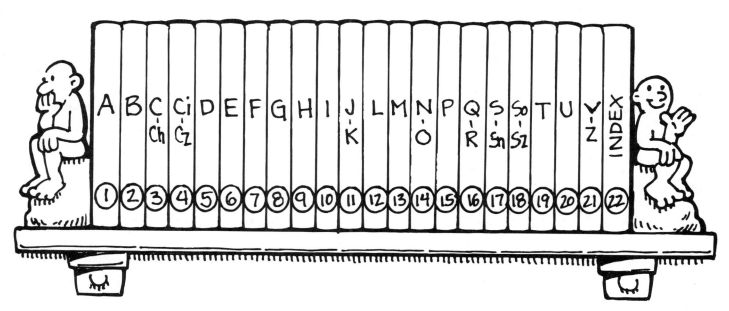

1 ____ the state flower of Illinois

2 ____ different breeds of horses

3 ____ *The Velveteen Rabbit*

4 ____ the Declaration of Independence

5 ____ the history of computers

6 ____ the color of a muskrat

7 ____ the date the first yo-yo was made

8 ____ process of making rubber

9 ____ names of cowboys

10 ____ the capital of Germany

11 ____ a list of topics in the encyclopedia

12 ____ the lifecycle of a caterpillar

13 ____ birthday of Abraham Lincoln

14 ____ how diamonds are mined

15 ____ phases of the moon

16 ____ President Bill Clinton

17 ____ date Alaska became a state

18 ____ number of Jupiter's moons

19 ____ first battle of the Civil War

20 ____ structure of a cell

Name _____   Date _____

Using References

USING REFERENCE MATERIALS

> **Almanac:** a yearly publication that includes lists, charts, and tables, and summarizes information from many different fields
> **Atlas:** a collection of maps; often contains population information
> **Book of Quotations:** a listing of well-known sayings, usually by famous people
> **Thesaurus:** a book of synonyms and antonyms
> **Reader's Guide to Periodical Literature:** an author/subject index of articles and stories published in magazines; it comes out once or twice a month

Read the summaries of the reference books. Then tell which reference book you might use to find the information below. Some topics may have more than one answer.

1 the name of the mountain ranges in Colorado _____

2 who said "live and let live" _____

3 number of gold medallists from China in 2000 Olympics _____

4 synonym of *unique* _____

5 rainfall in Taiwan _____

6 articles about aquarium maintenance _____

7 the opposite of *fierce* _____

8 recent developments in eye surgery _____

9 quotations by John Adams _____

10 countries in the Middle East _____

11 the height of Mount Everest _____

12 articles written by Alex Meyers _____

13 population of Chicago, IL _____

14 a more interesting word for *ugly* _____

15 baseball statistics for your favorite team _____

16 who said, "ask not what your country ..." _____

Reading a Coupon

CONSUMER READING

> ## 15% off Regularly Priced Games, Movies, Music, and Computer Software, any combination
>
> *Must be regularly priced merchandise. Not valid on sale items. Not valid with any other offer. Limit 5 items per coupon. Redeemable in store only. Coupon must be presented at time of sale. Must be used Monday–Friday. $50 minimum purchase. May not be redeemed for cash. Offer expires 7/17/06.

Use the coupon to answer the questions.

1 Can you use this coupon on more than one item? _____

2 Can you use this coupon for Internet purchases? _____

3 How much of a discount will you receive with this coupon? _____

4 How much money must you spend to redeem this coupon? _____

5 When does this coupon expire? _____

6 Which of the following can you **not** do with this coupon?
   a. buy 3 games
   b. buy regularly priced items
   c. use in the store
   d. make your purchase on Saturday

7 Which of the following is **not** a reason for the store to offer coupons?
   a. to get new customers in the store
   b. to sell old products to make room for new stock
   c. to keep customers coming back to the store
   d. to lose customers and profits

Name _____ Date _____

Reading a Recipe

CONSUMER READING

Caramel Apple Muffin Mix

Directions: Preheat oven to 375°.
Presoak apple packet in ¼ cup of HOT water for 10 minutes, or microwave in ¼ cup water for 1 minute. Combine package of muffin mix with ⅔ cup milk, 1 egg, 2 tablespoons oil, and undrained, presoaked apples. Stir until blended. Fill greased muffin cups ½ to ⅔ full. Mix small topping packet with 1 tablespoon melted butter or margarine. Add ½ teaspoon of mixture to center of each muffin. Bake 15–20 minutes or until done.

Use the recipe to answer the questions.

1 At what temperature should you bake the muffins? _____

2 How long do the muffins bake? _____

3 How many different packets are in this muffin mix? _____

4 How much milk do you need in this recipe? _____

5 How should you prepare the muffin cups? _____

6 What two ways can you prepare the apple packet? _____

7 How much muffin mix do you put in each muffin cup? _____

8 How many eggs do you need for this mix? _____

Reading Skills • 7–8 © 2004 Creative Teaching Press

Reading a Train Route

CONSUMER READING

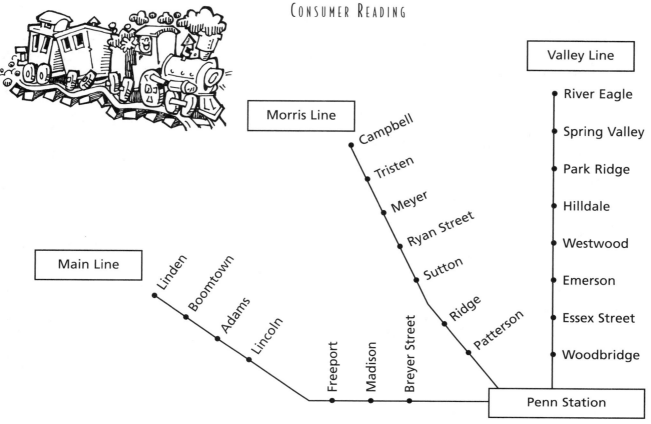

Use the train route to answer the questions.

1 What is the name of the main train station?_____

2 Which line has a stop named Meyer? _____

3 Leaving from Penn Station, what is the fourth stop on the Main Line?_____

4 Leaving from Penn Station, what is the last stop on the Valley Line?_____

5 How many stops are on the Morris Line? _____

6 Which line would you take to get to Essex Street? _____

7 Leaving Penn Station, how many stops would you make before Spring Valley? _____

8 Which line would you take to get to Boomtown? _____

9 Leaving from Penn Station, what stop is after Ridge? _____

10 Which line has the most stops? _____ How many does it have?_____

Reading Skills • 7–8 © 2004 Creative Teaching Press

Name _____ Date _____

Reading an Advertisement

Consumer Reading

The Abigal.

$64.99
originally $79.99

The Brittany.

$59.99
originally $74.99

The Celeste.

$49.99
originally $59.99

The Dariya.

$39.99
originally $49.99

The Esmerelda.

$64.99
originally $84.99

Use the advertisement to answer the questions.

1 Which shoe is the least expensive? _____

2 Which shoe or shoes have the greatest price reduction? _____

3 On which shoe will save you $10? _____

4 Which shoe or shoes are $15 off? _____

5 Which shoe had the highest original price? _____

6 Which shoe or shoes have the most expensive sale price? _____

7 How much would Abigail and Dariya shoes cost together on sale? _____

8 How much would Brittany and Esmerelda shoes cost together at the original price?

_____

Reading Skills • 7–8 © 2004 Creative Teaching Press

Name _____   Date _____

Reading a Promotional Offer

Consumer Reading

Get a Free CD

Send:
1. 3 UPC symbols from boxes of Sugar Drops,
   Crunchy Pops, or Rice Yummies
2. Your name, address, other information on
   the blank card
3. self-addressed, stamped envelope
4. $1.25 postage and handling

To:
The Free CD Offer
1111 Prize Way
Cool Stuff, CA 12345
Allow 4–6 weeks for delivery.

Use the promotional offer to answer the questions.

1 How long will it take to receive your CD? _____

2 How many UPC symbols are required for the free CD? _____

3 What products can be used for the UPC symbols? _____

4 How much postage and handling is needed for this offer? _____

5 Where should you send your materials? _____

6 Fill out the blank card with the information requested in the promotional offer.

Name _____

Address _____

Favorite color _____

Month of your birthday _____

Age _____

Circle one:

Favorite type of music: classical   rock   country   jazz   other

Reading Skills • 7–8 © 2004 Creative Teaching Press

Name _____ Date _____

Analyzing Poetry
ANALYZE NARRATIVE TEXTS

After Dark
Fireflies flash hello,
While crickets serenade
The last glimmer of day
Below the horizon.

Warm breezes
Give way to cool dark
And all that
Is night arises.

We creep through
The tall grass playing
Hide-and-seek with
Nocturnal surprises.

Read the poem and answer the questions.

1 This poem is mostly about
    a. crickets.
    b. the sun.
    c. night.
    d. hide-and-seek.

2 The word *nocturnal* relates to
    a. night.
    b. day.
    c. animal.
    d. new.

3 The purpose of this poem is to
    a. teach the reader about
      night.
    b. entertain the reader.
    c. persuade the reader to go
      outside.
    d. tell the reader how to play
      hide-and-seek.

4 The last word in the second stanza rhymes with what other word in the poem?
    a. glimmer
    b. noturnal
    c. playing
    d. surprises

5 The first stanza tells about all of the following EXCEPT
    a. fireflies.
    b. crickets.
    c. hide-and-seek.
    d. the sunset.

6 Which word from the poem means *sing to*?
    a. glimmer
    b. nocturnal
    c. creep
    d. serenade

Reading Skills • 7–8 © 2004 Creative Teaching Press

Analyzing a Journal Entry

ANALYZE NARRATIVE TEXTS

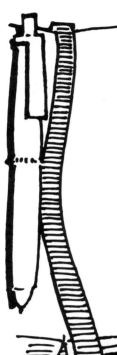

August 24

    Today we left on our trip to visit my cousins, Jordan and Shelby. We are driving for two days! I sure hope my brother won't bother me too much. So far we have traveled 200 miles. That seems so far, but we are not even halfway there.

August 25

    We stayed at a really fun hotel. There was a water park inside! I slept great after all that exercise. My brother and I are playing a license plate game. We're trying to find every state. So far I'm ahead with twenty. Only three more hours until we arrive at my cousins' house. I'm starting to get really excited!

August 26

    We had such a great night! I can't believe how much my cousins have changed. They are both so tall. We camped out in their backyard last night. I don't think anyone got much sleep, but we had a blast! I can't wait to see what happens today.

Read the journal entries and answer the questions.

1 Where is the writer going?
    a. to the mall
    b. to the beach
    c. to visit grandmother
    d. to visit cousins

2 How many journal entries did the writer make?
    a. 3
    b. 2
    c. 4
    d. 1

3 How do you know when each entry was made?
    a. each entry is numbered
    b. each entry is dated
    c. each entry is lettered
    d. you don't know

4 How long did it take the writer to reach her destination?
    a. 3 days
    b. 3 hours
    c. 200 miles
    d. 2 days

5 How can you tell the writer is having a good time? Use examples from the journal entries to support your answer.

_____

_____

Analyzing a Personal Narrative

ANALYZE NARRATIVE TEXTS

My grandparents had an interesting business when they were first married. They owned and operated an icehouse. What's an icehouse? Well, it's not a house made from ice. Actually, before people had refrigerators in their homes, they kept their food in large insulated boxes. Inside the boxes they placed big cubes of ice to keep the food cold. My grandfather bought ice from a large company and then delivered the big blocks to people's homes. Carrying all that ice made my grandfather very strong. My grandparents enjoyed their business for fourteen years. The invention of the electric refrigerator eliminated the need for icehouses. But that didn't stop my grandparents. They turned their icehouse into a candy store. They went from selling ice to selling sweets. I, for one, am very grateful!

Read the personal narrative and answer the questions.

1 Who is this story about?
- a. the narrator
- b. the narrator's parents
- c. the narrator's aunt and uncle
- d. the narrator's grandparents

2 What type of business did the grandparents own?
- a. general store
- b. icehouse
- c. box business
- d. refrigerator sales

3 Why did the grandparents begin selling candy?
- a. icehouses were no longer needed
- b. they like candy better than ice
- c. they moved to a new town
- d. their icehouse melted

4 How long did the grandparents have their first business?
- a. 10 years
- b. 20 years
- c. 14 years
- d. 8 years

5 What kind of people do you think the narrator's grandparents were? Use evidence from the narrative to support your answer.

_____

_____

_____

Name _____ Date _____

Analyzing a Biography

ANALYZE NARRATIVE TEXTS

Eleanor Roosevelt was a social activist, humanitarian, and crusader for human rights. She was also the wife of the thirty-second president of the United States, Franklin Delano Roosevelt.

Franklin D. Roosevelt became president in 1933, and Eleanor began her twelve-year career as one of this country's most active first ladies. Her husband had been stricken with polio and was confined to a wheelchair. Because of his disability, Eleanor traveled for him and reported on what she had observed.

She was also very involved in social causes. Prior to becoming first lady, Eleanor worked at the New York League of Women's Voters. She also established the Val-Kill Furniture Shop in Hyde Park, New York, to provide jobs for the unemployed.

As first lady, Eleanor worked tirelessly for civil rights causes for African Americans and women. She also had her own radio program and wrote a daily column called "My Day."

After her husband's death, Eleanor was appointed a United States delegate to the United Nations. She even helped to draft the U.N. Declaration of Human Rights. She lived a very full life until she died on November 7, 1962.

Read the narrative and answer the questions.

1 Eleanor Roosevelt was all of the following EXCEPT
- **a.** a social activist.
- **b.** first lady.
- **c.** a U.N. delegate.
- **d.** in a wheelchair.

2 Based on the passage, a *humanitarian* is most likely
- **a.** someone who sells things.
- **b.** someone who helps people.
- **c.** someone who is afraid to fly.
- **d.** someone who does not vote.

3 What is the root word of *unemployed*?
- **a.** unemploy
- **b.** ployed
- **c.** ploy
- **d.** employ

4 You can infer from the passage that Eleanor Roosevelt was
- **a.** a strong woman.
- **b.** an intelligent woman.
- **c.** well respected.
- **d.** all of the above.

5 The last line of the passage states that Mrs. Roosevelt led a very full life. Write at least three details from the passage that support this conclusion.

_____

_____

_____

Reading Skills • 7–8 © 2004 Creative Teaching Press

Analyzing a Business Letter

ANALYZE EXPOSITORY TEXTS

2416 Pine Street
Anywhere, NM 12345
September 25, 2008

Director—School Trip Planning
U.S. Department of Education
2101 State Street
Washington, D.C. 20036

Dear Director:
    I am an eighth grader at Trenton Middle School. We are planning a visit to the nation's capital. I am interested in receiving information about the field trip program.
    I would appreciate a copy of your advertised information packet. I am interested in the following information:
        1. a list of historical and government tour packages
        2. a list of recommended hotel locations
        3. the recommended tour group sizes and pricing information
    Thank you for your help.

Sincerely,

Mary Edinborough

Mary Edinborough

Read the letter and answer the questions.

1 Who is this letter written to?
    a. the Director of School Trip Planning
    b. the President of the United States
    c. the Director of the U.S. Dept. of Education
    d. the Principal of Trenton M. S.

2 What is the greeting in this letter?
    a. Director—School Trip Planning
    b. Sincerely
    c. Mary Edinborough
    d. Dear Director

3 Whose address appears at the top of this letter?
    a. the Director of School Trip Planning
    b. the Principal of Trenton M. S.
    c. Mary Edinborough
    d. the President of the United States

4 What is the closing in this letter?
    a. Director—School Trip Planning
    b. Sincerely
    c. Mary Edinborough
    d. Dear Director

5 Why did Mary write this letter? Use details from the letter in your answer.

_____

_____

Name _____ Date _____

Analyzing a How-to Passage

ANALYZE EXPOSITORY TEXTS

Did you ever wonder how your brain controls your body? A complicated system of signals, actions, and reactions is responsible. Different parts of the brain do different things.

The medulla controls certain muscles and glands. Its jobs include keeping your heart pumping, taking air into your lungs, and digesting food in your stomach.

The cerebellum is responsible for movement and balance. This area of the brain keeps you running and dancing. The cerebrum is the part of the brain that controls thinking, learning, remembering, and awareness. Sensations like hearing, smelling, tasting, and touching come from here.

Nerve cells act as pathways between our brain and the rest of our body. Messages are carried along these pathways of cells, and the brain sorts out the signals. Many parts work together to create our amazing central nervous system.

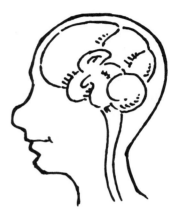

Read the passage and answer the questions.

1 Which of the following acts as a pathway for signals to and from the brain?
    a. cerebellum
    b. medulla
    c. nerve cells
    d. cerebrum

2 Which part of the brain controls the sense of taste?
    a. cerebellum
    b. medulla
    c. nerve cells
    d. cerebrum

3 The medulla does all of the following EXCEPT
    a. keeps your heart beating.
    b. takes air into the lungs.
    c. tells stomach to digest.
    d. helps you keep your balance.

4 Nerve cells are most like a
    a. a roadblock.
    b. a highway.
    c. a lake.
    d. a wheel.

5 Write a title that describes the main idea of this passage.

_____

6 What is the author's purpose for writing the passage?

_____

Name _____ Date _____

Analyzing a Newspaper Article

Analyze Expository Texts

The Claremont Huskies set a record last night for most consecutive wins. The team won its ninth game in a row, beating the Fisher Flyers by a score of 74–56. Sam James scored a career high of 32 points. Five of his baskets were from three-point range.

"These players have real team spirit. They work hard and support each other," said Coach Riley. "That is why they are winners."

The team heads into the regional tournament with a 15–2 record, the best in school history. While hopeful for a good showing, the team is proud of its accomplishments to this point.

"We already feel like winners," said star forward Dan Brown.

The first regional game will be played at 8:30 p.m. on Friday. The Huskies will challenge the 10–7 Gifford Tigers at Gifford.

Read the newspaper article and answer the questions.

1 What sport is discussed in this article?
    a. basketball
    b. baseball
    c. soccer
    d. tennis

2 What is the name of the team with the most consecutive wins?
    a. Fisher Flyers
    b. Gifford Tigers
    c. Claremont Huskies
    d. none of the above

3 In the last sentence, what does 10–7 stand for?
    a. the time of the game
    b. the number of the star player
    c. the points scored in the game
    d. wins and losses of the Gifford Tigers

4 What team does Dan Brown play for?
    a. Gifford Tigers
    b. Claremont Huskies
    c. Fisher Flyers
    d. none of the above

5 Why do you think the team already feels like winners? Support your answer with evidence from the article.

_____

_____

_____

Reading Skills • 7–8 © 2004 Creative Teaching Press

Analyzing a Compare/Contrast Passage

ANALYZE EXPOSITORY TEXTS

Dogs and cats are popular choices for house pets. While they are both well suited to family life, they require very different levels and kinds of care.

Many people choose dogs as pets. A dog is considered more high maintenance than a cat. Dogs must be taken outside several times a day for bathroom breaks. They also need exercise, and most breeds should be walked once or twice each day. Large breed dogs require a great deal of food in order to maintain their health. They also should be given fresh water daily. Dogs are very loving animals. They can be trained, and most dogs interact frequently with their owners.

Cats are also a popular pet choice. They tend to be low maintenance. Cats use a litter box for their bathroom, so they do not depend on their owners to take them outside. However, the litter box must be cleaned frequently. Cats find their own methods of exercise, often running around for seemingly no reason. They sleep a great deal of their day, so they don't need much attention. Cats tend to be small animals and eat little compared to dogs. While many cats have a loving side, they do not seek to please their owners in the same way as dogs. They are not usually willing to be trained and seek affection only on their own terms.

Both animals provide great joy and love for their owners. Regardless of which kind of pet you choose both will enrich your life.

Read the compare/contrast passage and answer the questions.

❶ Draw and label a Venn diagram comparing and contrasting dogs and cats. Use information from the passage.

❷ Which kind of pet would you choose to own? Explain your choice and use examples from the passage and your own experiences to support your answer.

_____

_____

_____

_____

Name _____ Date _____

Math

CONTENT AREA READING

Angles are formed by two rays that have the same endpoint. This endpoint is called the **vertex.** Angles can be found anywhere lines or line segments intersect. Angles are named for the way they relate to 90° or 180°. When an angle is less than 90°, it is called **acute.** An angle that is exactly 90° is called a **right angle.** An angle greater than 90° and less than 180° is called **obtuse.**

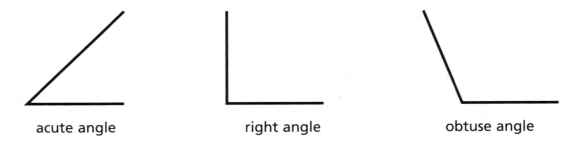

acute angle   right angle   obtuse angle

Read the passage and diagrams and answer the questions.

1 A **vertex** is
   a. a right angle.
   b. two rays.
   c. intersecting segments.
   d. the endpoint of an angle.

3 A **right angle** is
   a. 180°.
   b. 90°.
   c. 10°.
   d. more than 90°.

2 An angle that is more than 90° but less than 180° is called
   a. right.
   b. acute.
   c. vertex.
   d. obtuse.

4 All of the following are true EXCEPT
   a. angles are found anywhere lines intersect.
   b. a right angle is 90°.
   c. acute and obtuse angles are the same.
   d. angles have an endpoint.

5 Draw an acute angle and an obtuse angle that are different from the ones shown above. Label the **vertex** and **rays** of each angle.

Reading Skills • 7–8 © 2004 Creative Teaching Press

Social Studies

CONTENT AREA READING

President Abraham Lincoln greatly wished to end the Civil War. He declared that he would do so in any way necessary. On January 1, 1863, Lincoln issued an order known as the Emancipation Proclamation. Essentially, this order declared that all slaves in the territories opposing the Union, namely the Southern Confederate states, were free. While this declaration did not immediately lead to the freedom of any slaves, it did spark fear in the Southern slaveholders. They worried that a rebellion would begin amongst slaves, so they denounced the proclamation. The order did have several immediate effects though. It lifted the war to a level of crusade for human freedom. It also enabled the Union to recruit black soldiers for military service. One hundred eighty thousand new recruits joined to fight against Confederate soldiers. Lincoln considered this order to be the central act of his administration and the greatest event of the nineteenth century. It led to the freedom of all slaves and the ratification of the Thirteenth Amendment in December of 1865.

Read the passage and answer the questions.

1 What year was the Emancipation Proclamation issued?
- **a.** 1865
- **b.** 1880
- **c.** 1863
- **d.** 1800

2 The proclamation did all of the following EXCEPT
- **a.** immediately free all slaves.
- **b.** make the Civil War about freedom for all.
- **c.** enable black men to enlist.
- **d.** lead to the Thirteenth Amendment.

3 The proclamation was issued by
- **a.** the Confederate Army.
- **b.** the Union Army.
- **c.** Europe.
- **d.** Abraham Lincoln.

4 You can conclude that the Thirteenth Amendment
- **a.** ended the Civil War.
- **b.** prohibited slavery.
- **c.** prohibited proclamations.
- **d.** created a new army.

5 Write a one- to two-line summary of the Emancipation Proclamation. Use only the most important information in your summary.

_____

_____

_____

Name _____ Date _____

Science

CONTENT AREA READING

Green plants have the ability to make their own food with the help of a few simple substances. The process is known as **photosynthesis.** The first step of this process occurs when water is taken up through the roots of the plant and carried to the leaves. Then carbon dioxide, given off by human and animal respiration, is taken into the plant through the leaves. It spreads to the cells containing a green pigment called **chlorophyll.** Plants use chlorophyll to absorb some of the sun's light energy. Then the plant converts this radiant energy into chemical energy. The water in the plant is broken into oxygen, which is given off by the plant, and hydrogen. The hydrogen works with the carbon dioxide in the plant to create simple sugars. These simple sugars are stored as food for the plant.

Read the passage and answer the questions.

1 Photosynthesis takes place
  a. in plants.
  b. in the air.
  c. in the sun.
  d. in the ground.

2 Which of the following is not a part of the process of photosynthesis?
  a. sunlight
  b. chlorophyll
  c. water
  d. soil

3 **Chlorophyll** is
  a. found in water.
  b. a mixture of carbon and hydrogen.
  c. a green pigment found in plants.
  d. sugar stored in plants.

4 Sunlight causes water to be broken into
  a. hydrogen and carbon dioxide.
  b. carbon dioxide and oxygen.
  c. hydrogen and nitrogen.
  d. hydrogen and oxygen.

5 What effect do plants have on human respiration? Use information from the passage to explain your answer.

_____

_____

_____

_____

Reading Skills • 7–8 © 2004 Creative Teaching Press

Health

CONTENT AREA READING

Maintaining good dental health is as easy as following a few simple steps. The first step involves eating a healthy, balanced diet. You should also avoid sugary snacks and drinks. Instead, drink water treated with fluoride. Fluoride is a natural element that when absorbed into your body helps cells create stronger tooth enamel. This makes you less likely to develop dental cavities. A second step to a healthy smile is good brushing and flossing habits. You should brush your teeth for 2½ to 3 minutes at least twice a day. Flossing once a day also helps to remove food and plaque that can build up between teeth. Both tasks make for cleaner teeth and gums and fresh breath. Last, but not least, visit your dentist regularly, at least twice a year. These preventative checkups and cleanings enable your dentist to spot any hidden problems and take care of them before they become big, painful issues.

Read the passage and answer the questions.

1 All of the following can lead to cavities EXCEPT
   a. sugary snacks.
   b. not flossing.
   c. brushing daily.
   d. skipping checkups.

3 Fluoride is
   a. a man-made product.
   b. often added to drinking water.
   c. damaging to tooth enamel.
   d. not necessary for children.

2 What is the recommended amount of time for brushing your teeth?
   a. 2½ to 3 minutes
   b. 5 minutes
   c. 1 to 2 minutes
   d. as long as you want

4 How often does the passage suggest you should visit the dentist?
   a. four times a year
   b. every one to two years
   c. twice a year
   d. none of the above

5 Write a set of directions to help someone develop healthy dental practices. Use the information from the passage to help you prepare your answer. Use the back of this page if necessary.

_____

_____

_____

Art

Did you know that a quilt or a hand-knit sweater is actually a piece of art? Both of these are examples of **textiles,** or artwork made from cloth fibers, such as yarn. **Fibers** are threadlike materials that come from animals, plants, and chemicals. Silk and wool are examples of animal fibers. Linen, flax, and cotton are examples of plant fibers, and nylon and rayon are examples of fibers made from chemicals.

Most textile and fiber art is created using techniques called **weaving** and **stitchery.** These techniques are ancient artforms, but they remain popular among craftspeople today. Weaving involves interlocking threads, or using fiberlike materials to create fabric. While most modern-day weaving is done in a factory, traditional weavers use a tool called a loom. Artisans who create textiles with stitchery use a needle, thread or yarn, and cloth. Appliqué and quilting are two techniques used to create fabric art.

As you examine a piece of fabric, a blanket, or clothing, pay attention to the detail and variation. Try to determine the process used to create the piece of fabric art.

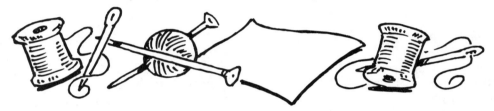

Read the passage and answer the questions.

1 Two techniques for creating fiber art are
   a. fibers and textile.
   b. weaving and stitchery.
   c. looms and needles.
   d. linen and flax.

2 A textile is
   a. threadlike materials.
   b. a wooden frame.
   c. a type of needle.
   d. artwork made of cloth fibers.

3 Which of the following is a plant fiber?
   a. nylon
   b. rayon
   c. flax
   d. silk

4 A synonym for *craftsperson* is
   a. technique.
   b. artisan.
   c. stitchery.
   d. appliqué.

5 List 5 items, other than those listed in the passage, that are examples of textiles.

_____

_____

Reading Skills • 7–8 © 2004 Creative Teaching Press

Answer Key

Naming Pairs (page 5)

1. antonyms
2. antonyms
3. synonyms
4. antonyms
5. synonyms
6. antonyms
7. synonyms
8. antonyms
9. antonyms
10. synonyms
11. synonyms
12. synonyms

Sentences will vary.

Word Match (page 6)

1. damp, dry
2. sufficient, deficient
3. flunk, pass
4. disrespectful, polite
5. timid, bold
6. scald, freeze
7. assist, hinder
8. provoke, soothe
9. keep, destroy
10. shut, open

Story Time Synonyms (page 7)

1. j
2. a
3. n
4. k
5. i
6. g
7. b
8. m
9. c
10. h
11. e
12. f
13. l
14. d
15. Answers will vary. Possible answers include: The courageous small garment-maker

Interesting Words (page 8)

Answers will vary.
Possible answers include:

1. hard
2. arduous
3. effortless
4. simple

5. chilly
6. nippy
7. hot
8. sweltering

9. frightened
10. fearful
11. unafraid
12. calm

13. dim
14. unlit
15. fair
16. bright

17. oppressive
18. hefty
19. light
20. weightless

21. cheerful
22. merry
23. sorrowful
24. angry

Prefix Skills (page 9)

1. f
2. j
3. h
4. a
5. i
6. e
7. d
8. g
9. c
10. b

Suffix Skills (page 10)

1. g
2. f
3. h
4. i
5. j
6. c
7. a
8. b
9. e
10. d

Breaking Words (page 11)

1. fancy   ful
2. break able
3. smoky   ness
4. mis   treat
5. happy   ly
6. music   ian
7. home   ward
8. non   sense
9. bi   cycle
10. geology   ist
11. history   ian
12. jury   or
13. re   act
14. in   door
15. change   able
16. theory   ist
17. inter   act
18. para   phrase
19. friend   ship
20. sub   marine

Sentence Sense (page 14)

1. capital
2. passed
3. advice
4. than
5. conscience
6. lose
7. choose
8. except
9. effect
10. lie
11. rise
12. cooperation
13. lend
14. farther
15. assure
16. recent
17. confident
18. device
19. well
20. thorough

Crossword Puzzler (page 12)

Across

3. nontoxic
7. actress
8. retrospective
9. geology

Down

1. salvage
2. natural
4. triangle
5. pseudonym
6. simplify

Make the Right Choice (page 15)

1. raise
2. dessert
3. lie
4. rise
5. effect
6. wonder
7. desert
8. lay
9. wander
10. affect

Definition Decision (page 13)

1. personnel—employees, staff
2. personal—private
3. bibliography—a list of authors' works
4. biography—a written history of a person's life
5. decent—good; having strong morals
6. descent—process of moving down
7. recent—current
8. resent—to feel annoyed
9. devise—to plan
10. device—a piece of equipment
11. access—ability to enter
12. excess—more than needed

Correct or Incorrect? (page 16)

1. I
2. C
3. C
4. C
5. I
6. C
7. I
8. C
9. C
10. I
11. I
12. C
13. C
14. I
15. C
16. I
17. I
18. C
19. C
20. I

Finding Analogies (page 17)

1. sphere
2. jet
3. trunk
4. attic
5. destroy
6. autumn
7. new
8. early
9. vegetable
10. adult

Figure It Out (page 18)

1. flour
2. text
3. brick
4. stack
5. inventor
6. sanitary
7. mathematics
8. stationery
9. branch
10. teeth
11. proud
12. composite

Sentences will vary.

Analogy Puzzler (page 19)

Across

2. window
7. bike
8. theater

Down

1. stir
3. doctor
4. library
5. ink
6. laugh

Mind Challenge (page 20)

1. d
2. b
3. c
4. a
5. b
6. c
7. b
8. b
9. d
10. a

Everyday Idioms (page 21)

1. c
2. g
3. j
4. i
5. a
6. f
7. d
8. e
9. h
10. b

Select a Simile (page 22)

1. b
2. b
3. a
4. c
5. a
6. d
7. a
8. b

Movie Metaphors (page 23)

1. The snowstorm is a fierce creature.
2. The music she plays is a powerful medicine that calms you instantly.
3. The plot is a roller coaster of poorly related events.
4. Her disabled sister is a treasure to be cherished.

Identifying Figurative Language (page 24)

1. I
2. I
3. S
4. M
5. S
6. S
7. M
8. I
9. I
10. S
11. M
12. S
13. M
14. I
15. M
16. S
17. M
18. I
19. S
20. S

Homophones (page 25)

1. stationery
2. principal
3. whether
4. their
5. minor
6. threw
7. forward
8. lessen
9. patients
10. by
11. past
12. capital
13. shear
14. bail
15. matte

Letter Home (page 26)

1. Aunt
2. week
3. plane
4. hour
5. by
6. sail
7. would
8. pair
9. I
10. meet
11. know
12. two
13. wait
14. There
15. see
16. write
17. hear

Homographs (page 27)

1. g, o
2. b, i
3. a, u
4. k, s
5. d, x
6. m, w
7. c, j
8. e, p
9. h, n
10. t, v
11. l, z
12. f, q
13. r, y

Homograph Logic (page 28)

1. close
2. address
3. console
4. compress
5. wind
6. duck
7. saw
8. fine
9. tear
10. bear
11. minute
12. project
13. sage
14. store
15. refuse
16. trip

Conquering Context Clues (page 29)

1. country
2. worried
3. sleepy
4. interested
5. baby
6. food line
7. puny
8. make up something
9. effects
10. relatives

Meaning Sleuth (page 30)

1. a	4. d
2. c	5. b
3. b	6. d

Reading for Clues (page 31)

1. d	4. d
2. a	5. a
3. b	6. b

Dictionary Detective (page 32)

1. a
2. b
3. c
4. b
5. d
6. a
7. c
8. b
9. c
10. d

Human Body Classification (page 33)

Answers may appear in various orders.

System	Parts	
muscular	deltoids	biceps
repiratory	nose	lungs
skeletal	ribs	collarbone
circulatory	blood	heart
digestive	intestines	stomach

Classify Details (page 34)

Current situation: littered; dirty water; broken glass; dangerous to children; animals could be harmed
How we can help: organize a cleanup crew; pick up our own garbage; clean graffiti
Benefits of a clean park: beautiful to look at; safe place to play

Classified Ads (page 35)

1. Library Assistant; Cleaning Crew
2. Lifeguard
3. Lifeguard; Babysitter
4. Babysitter; Library Assistant; Baker's Assistant
5. Lifeguard; Library Assistant
6. Lifeguard

Classifying History (page 36)

Washington: first president; was a general

Jefferson: wrote the Declaration of Independence; bought the Louisiana Purchase

Lincoln: Gettysburg Address; was assassinated; ended slavery; the tallest president

Kennedy: was assassinated; youngest president; sparked space exploration

Story Ordering (page 37)

1. 3
   5
   2
   1
   4

2. 3
   1
   2
   5
   4

3. 3
   1
   4
   5
   2

Note Card Mix-Up (page 38)

1—Anne Frank was born June 12, 1929 in Frankfurt, Germany.

2—Anne was a bright student, but she was forced to leave her school to attend a Jewish school.

3—Anne and her family moved into their secret hiding place to escape the Gestapo.

4—In her diary, Anne wrote her deepest thoughts and keen observations about the others in hiding with her.

5—Her family was discovered and arrested.

6—The Gestapo left Anne's diary behind, believing the papers were unimportant.

7—Anne died from typhus in Bergen-Belsen, a German concentration camp.

8—After the war, Anne's diary was given to Otto Frank, the only survivor of the family.

What's the Order? (page 39)

2
7
3
1
5
6
4

Order the Steps (page 40)

3
6
1
7
4
5
2

Brownie Recipe (page 41)

1. 2
2. 4
   6
   5
   3
   2
   1
3. adding nuts
4. 350°
5. 45 minutes

Using a Flowchart (page 42)

1. take your temperature
2. call doctor during office hours
3. no
4. go to the emergency room
5. sore throat and temperature over 100°

Map It! (page 43)

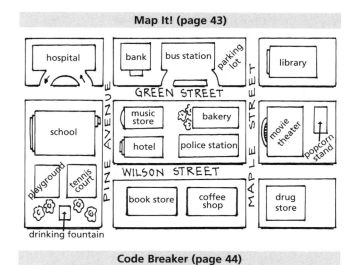

Code Breaker (page 44)

The secret to success is paying close attention to the details and never giving up.

Find the Cause or Effect (page 45)

Answers will vary. Possible answers include:

1. Harriet was strong and determined.
2. She joined the Underground Railroad.
3. She was not worried about her own safety.
4. He learned from his failures.
5. He is credited with over 1,000 inventions.
6. She voted in Rochester.
7. She was arrested.
8. She fought for suffrage.
9. The Nineteenth Amendment is also called the Susan B. Anthony Amendment.

Just Because (page 46)

1. b   4. c
2. c   5. d
3. c   6. b

Frederick Douglass (page 47)

1. b
2. d
3. Douglass spoke about his enslavement, published the *North Star,* served as an advisor to President Lincoln, and recruited black men into the Union Army.

The American Revolution (page 48)

1. c
2. d
3. the Currency Act

Inference Practice (page 49)

1. c
2. b
3. d

What a Character! (page 50)

1. c
2. d
3. b

What's Happening? (page 51)

1. A baby's first steps
2. The Gettysburg Address or President Lincoln's speech
3. Braces removed
4. Rosa Parks story or beginning of Civil Rights Movement
5. Driving test

Infer the Meaning (page 52)

1. b
2. d
3. d
4. c

Which Is Which? (page 53)

1. F
2. O
3. F
4. O
5. O
6. O
7. F
8. F
9. O
10. F
11. F
12. F
13. O
14. O
15. O
16. F
17. F

Identifying Fact and Opinion (page 54)

1. b
2. b
3. a
4. b

Sorting Facts and Opinions (page 55)

1. a   c
   b   d
   e   f

2. a   b
   d   c
   e
   f

Analyze an Editorial (page 56)

1. b
2. b
3. d

Story Summary (page 57)

1. a
2. b
3. Answers will vary. Possible answers include: A New World

Movie Buff (page 58)

1. It Does Come Back
2. Polar Ice Cap
3. Professional Dreamer
4. Wild, Wild West
5. It Does Come Back
6. Answers will vary.

Sum It Up (page 59)

Answers will vary. Possible answers include:
1. Benefits of gardening
Summary: Besides giving you exercise, growing your own garden allows you to have very fresh vegetables while controlling the chemicals used to grow them.

2. Reading is a hobby for everyone
Summary: Reading helps you learn, entertains you, reaches you on a personal level, and gives you freedom.

Short Summaries (page 60)

Answers will vary. Possible answers include:
1. The purpose of fables
Summary: Not only are fables entertaining, they have educational value as well.

2. We must learn more about the effects of pollution
Summary: Pollution is damaging our world and we must learn about it in order to make better choices.

First or Third (page 61)

1. T
2. T
3. F
4. F
5. F
6. T
7. T
8. F
9. T
10. F
11. F
12. F
13. T
14. F

First to Third; Third to First (page 62)

Answers will vary. Possible answers include:
1. I left my book on the bus.
2. We play soccer after school.
3. He typed his paper on the computer in his mom's office.
4. Her uncle gave her a skateboard for her birthday.
5. What color are my eyes?
6. I took the shortcut home from my lesson.
7. Does she need to have her dad sign this permission slip?
8. His basketball coach said he had real potential.
9. The dog chased her around the block and up her driveway.
10. My grandmother lives three hours from my house.

Fairy Tale Views (page 63)

1. g
2. f
3. h
4. c
5. a
6. e
7. a
8. b
9. d
10. f
11. e
12. a

Pick a Point (page 64)

1. first person point of view
2. first person point of view
3. third person point of view
4. first person point of view

What Do They Want? (page 65)

1. c
2. b
3. a
4. b

What's Happening? (page 66)

Answers will vary. Possible answers include:
1. Carmela got food poisoning from the chicken.
2. Brett went straight to work from then on.
3. Lisa is running a hurdle race.
4. Benjamin won the lottery.
5. Carlos and Tina are on a roller coaster.

What's the Word? (page 67)

Answers will vary. Possible answers include:
1. repay
2. longing for the past
3. be overcome by
4. mental image
5. a glass container with plants and rocks
6. made up
7. chains
8. kindness

Experimental Conclusions (page 68)

Answers will vary. Possible answers include:
1. The rock is heavier than the cup of marbles.
2. Jumping rope is more strenuous than walking up stairs.
3. Baking soda reacts with vinegar but not plain water.
4. Sunlight is necessary for healthy leaves to grow.

It's All in the Title (page 69)

1. b
2. c
3. d

Name the Article (page 70)

1. History Brought to Life
2. One Student's Triumph
3. Lunch Room Rules
4. Future Plans Announced

Main Idea (page 71)

1. c
2. d
3. a

Statement Identification (page 72)

1. S
   M
   S
   S
   S

2. S
   S
   S
   M
   S

3. S
   S
   M
   S
   S

4. M
   S
   S
   S
   S

5. S
   S
   S
   M
   S

Which One Doesn't Belong? (page 73)

1. Camping trailers are a good way to enjoy the outdoors.
2. The museum has an exhibit on Egypt.
3. The North Star was often used by sailors to navigate their ships.
4. The Northern people were often called "Yankees."
5. Keyboarding lessons are helpful when you want to type quickly.
6. Doctors see many different patients in the course of a day.

Volunteer Persuasion (page 74)

1. d
2. c
3. b
4. a

What Happened Next? (page 75)

1. i
2. h
3. q
4. g
5. o
6. m
7. d
8. a
9. n
10. b
11. t
12. r
13. k
14. p
15. j
16. l
17. s
18. f
19. c
20. e

And Then . . . (page 76)

1. b
2. c
3. a
4. d

What Is That About? (page 77)

1. b
2. d
3. b
4. c
5. b
6. a
7. b
8. c
9. d
10. c

More Predictions (page 78)

1. d
2. d
3. a
4. c

Who and Where? (page 79)

1. b   3. a
2. a   4. c
5. Answers will vary.

Dialogue Drawings (page 80)

Answers will vary.

It's All about the Moral (page 81)

1. c
2. d

Plot Line (page 82)

1. 4
   1
   2
   5
   3

2. 5
   3
   1
   4
   2

3. 1
   5
   2
   4
   3

Reading a Table of Contents (page 83)

1. Math
2. 15
3. 69
4. 55
5. Graphing
6. 12
7. 7
8. 99
9. 7
10. 10

Using a Glossary (page 84)

1. force
2. the basic living unit of an organism
3. 2
4. point on which a lever is supported and turns
5. 11
6. acceleration
7. negatively charged particle that moves around the nucleus of an atom
8. d

Using an Index (page 85)

1. 27, 293   7. 30, 45, 289
2. 24   8. 301
3. 45–46   9. 19, 53, 103, 146
4. 292   10. 135, 269
5. 114, 118, 239   11. 146–150
6. 36
12. zoo; 24, 35, 48–51, 167, 214, 278

Understanding a Bibliography (page 86)

1. *The Bill of Rights and You*
2. 35–46
3. Dennis Hemrich
4. *New York Times*
5. 4
6. 2004
7. Chandler Press
8. *Atlantic*
9. December 2001
10. San Francisco, CA

Interpreting a Bar Graph (page 87)

Numerical answers may vary slightly.
1. Cheetah
2. Squirrel
3. 40 mph
4. Coyote, 13 mph
5. 25 mph
6. Rabbit
7. 45 mph
8. 58 mph

Interpreting Charts (page 88)

1. 21%
2. Nitrogen
3. 99%
4. 22%
5. 79%
6. May; $10
7. $50
8. $30
9. $20
10. negative; $40

Interpreting a Table (page 89)

1. Tokyo, Japan; 26,440,000
2. 16,640,000
3. India
4. Bombay; Calcutta
5. 2
6. 13,427,000
7. 13,522,000
8. 4,615,000
9. 39,485,000
10. Tokyo, Japan; Mexico City, Mexico; Bombay, India; São Paulo, Brazil; New York City, U.S.

Interpreting a Timeline (page 90)

1. February 20, 1962
2. Valentina Tereshkova
3. Russia (Soviet Union)
4. December, 1972
5. Soviet Alexei Leonov is the first person to walk in space.
6. Neil Armstrong
7. July 20, 1969
8. 10 months
9. May 14, 1973
10. Yuri Gagarin

Interpreting a Diagram (page 91)

1. Bread, Cereal, Rice, & Pasta
2. Fats, Oils, & Sweets
3. 2–4 servings
4. Answers will vary.
5. Answers will vary.
6. not very often
7. 2–3 servings
8. the number of servings of different kinds of foods you should eat each day

Using a Thesaurus (page 92)

1. 4
2. adjective, noun
3. frigid
4. illness
5. Answers will vary.
6. 440
7. Answers will vary.
8. 441
9. Answers will vary.

Using a Dictionary (page 93)

1. b
2. a
3. d
4. b
5. c
6. a
7. a
8. d

Using an Internet Search Engine (page 94)

1. rainfall
2. history of dogs
3. A, B
4. D
5. C, D
6. C
7. A
8. C

Using an Encyclopedia (page 95)

1. 10
2. 9
3. 20
4. 5
5. 4
6. 13
7. 21
8. 16
9. 4
10. 8
11. 22
12. 3
13. 12
14. 5
15. 13
16. 4
17. 1
18. 11
19. 4
20. 3

Using References (page 96)

1. Atlas
2. Book of Quotations
3. Almanac
4. Thesaurus
5. Almanac
6. Reader's Guide to Periodical Literature
7. Thesaurus
8. Reader's Guide to Periodical Literature
9. Book of Quotations
10. Atlas
11. Atlas; Almanac
12. Reader's Guide to Periodical Literature
13. Almanac; Atlas
14. Thesaurus
15. Almanac
16. Book of Quotations

Reading a Coupon (page 97)

1. yes
2. no
3. 15% off
4. at least $50
5. 7/17/06
6. d
7. d

Reading a Recipe (page 98)

1. 375°
2. 15–20 minutes
3. 3 packets
4. 2/3 cup
5. grease them
6. soak packet in 1/4 cup hot water for 10 minutes or microwave packet in 1/4 cup of water for 1 minute
7. fill 1/2–2/3 full
8. 1

Reading a Train Route (page 99)

1. Penn Station
2. Morris Line
3. Lincoln
4. River Eagle
5. 8
6. Valley Line
7. 6
8. Main Line
9. Sutton
10. Valley Line; 9

Reading an Advertisement (page 100)

1. The Dariya
2. The Esmerelda
3. The Celeste and the Dariya
4. The Abigail and the Brittany
5. The Esmerelda
6. The Abigail and the Esmerelda
7. $104.98
8. $159.98

Reading a Promotional Offer (page 101)

1. 4–6 weeks
2. 3
3. Sugar Drops, Crunchy Pops, Rice Yummies
4. $1.25
5. 1111 Prize Way, Cool Stuff, CA 12345
6. Answers will vary.

Analyzing Poetry (page 102)

1. c
2. a
3. b
4. d
5. c
6. d

Analyzing a Journal Entry (page 103)

1. d
2. a
3. b
4. d
5. Answers will vary. Possible answers include: The writer says they stayed at a fun hotel, and she is very excited. Later the writer says that they had a blast.

Analyzing a Personal Narrative (page 104)

1. d
2. b
3. a
4. c
5. Answers will vary. Possible answers include: They were hard-working people. We learn that the grandfather had to carry the big ice blocks. They were also resilient because when the need for their business was gone, instead of giving up, they started a different business.

Analyzing a Biography (page 105)

1. d
2. b
3. d
4. d
5. Answers will vary. Possible answers include: She traveled for her husband, the President. She worked for many social causes. She was a delegate for the United Nations.

Analyzing a Business Letter (page 106)

1. a
2. d
3. c
4. b

5. Answers will vary. Possible answers include: She wrote this letter to request information to help plan the school trip.

Analyzing a How-to Passage (page 107)

1. c
2. d
3. d
4. b

5. Answers will vary. Possible answers include: Parts of the Brain

6. to teach or explain how your brain works

Analyzing a Newspaper Article (page 108)

1. a
2. c
3. d
4. b

5. Answers will vary. Possible answers include: The coach says that the team works well together and supports each other. They probably have a lot of fun. They have also set a record for the most consecutive wins.

Analyzing a Compare/Contrast Passage (page 109)

Answers will vary. Possible answers include:

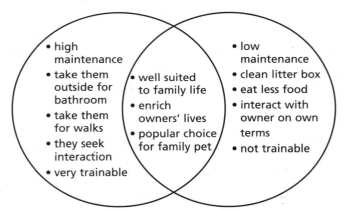

- high maintenance
- take them outside for bathroom
- take them for walks
- they seek interaction
- very trainable

- well suited to family life
- enrich owners' lives
- popular choice for family pet

- low maintenance
- clean litter box
- eat less food
- interact with owner on own terms
- not trainable

Math (page 110)

1. d
2. d
3. b
4. c

5. Answers will vary.

Social Studies (page 111)

1. c
2. a
3. d
4. b

5. Answers will vary. Possible answers include: The Emancipation Proclamation was an order that outlawed slavery in the Southern states. It led to slavery being outlawed in all states through the Thirteenth Amendment.

Science (page 112)

1. a
2. d
3. c
4. d

5. Answers will vary. Possible answers include: Plants give off oxygen, which humans need to breathe. Plants take in carbon dioxide, which humans breathe out.

Health (page 113)

1. c
2. a
3. b
4. c

5. Answers will vary. Possible answers include: 1. Eat a healthy diet and avoid sugary snacks and drinks. 2. Brush and floss daily. 3. Visit your dentist at least twice a year.

Art (page 114)

1. b
2. d
3. c
4. b

5. Answers will vary. Possible answers include: rug, curtain, couch cover, pillow, hat